Veterinary Advice for Greyhound Owners

JOHN KONKHE

Photography: Barbara Kelly

RINGPRESS

Published by Ringpress Books Ltd,
Spirella House, Bridge Road,
Letchworth, Herts, SG6 4ET.

Discounts available for bulk orders
Contact the Special Sales Manager at
the above address. Telephone (0462) 674177

Distributed to the Book Trade in the United Kingdom by
Bookpoint Ltd.
39 Milton Park, Abingdon, Oxon OX14 4TD
Telephone 0235 835001

First Published 1993

ISBN 0 948955 23 6

Printed and bound in Singapore
by Kyodo Printing Co

THIS BOOK IS DEDICATED TO THE MEMORY OF

BARBARA KELLY

who, as my personal assistant, made a major
contribution to the production of this book

CONTENTS

PREFACE

I have had the pleasure of writing for the *The Greyhound Star,* Britain's popular monthly greyhound racing paper, for a number of years, and I have covered a wide range of common, and not-so-common greyhound health problems. Over the years, readers have kept a continuous flow of letters describing problems with their greyhounds and seeking advice through the column, and these have now been compiled as a valuable handbook on greyhound health. They cover a wide range of topics, and provide the answer to many of the problems that may be encountered when training racing greyhounds.

Obviously it is difficult to give specific advice on injuries without examining the greyhound in question. However, most readers have provided full and graphic details of the case history, symptoms and treatments given to their greyhounds. In fact, I have been most impressed by the detail contained in the letters – it is obvious that greyhound trainers are a very observant and astute group of animal lovers.

My answers have had to be kept to a reasonable length in order to provide informative and useful practical advice to explain, or provide a remedy for the problem. Some of the original answers have been updated to include new recommendations for treatment, and answers have been revised and added to where necessary.

The letters and their answers have been arranged into specific problem areas of: Breeding, Nutrition, Lameness, Respiratory Diseases, Breeding General Health Care and Miscellaneous Problems. Sub-groups within these broad categories should enable you to locate an answer to a similar problem that you may have with your greyhound. Although in many cases the answer was straightforward, in others I had to inquire from colleagues and other greyhound veterinarians, seeking their advice on some of the queries raised.

I hope that you will find this collection of letters useful and of practical help in caring for, and maintaining health and performance in your greyhounds. I congratulate *The Greyhound Star* in taking the initiative to compile not just another greyhound book based on trainers' experiences, but something that will be of practical benefit in the care of our wonderful racing animals.

JOHN R. KOHNKE,
Veterinary Surgeon.

Chapter One

GENERAL HEALTH CARE

EXERCISE

1. Q I have an 11-month-old greyhound who has just started trialling once a month. We have done this twice, as we think he enjoys it because he is chasing the hare. Could you tell us if he is too young to start trialling or if it is beneficial to him?

A It is quite safe to gallop a young dog over short distances to help strengthen up his bones and muscle structure. However, it is unwise to force a dog to trial with other dogs in a competitive trial, particularly around a circle track where his immaturity and lack of fitness may lead to injury. The risk of 'shin soreness' or metacarpal soreness in the front feet is increased when young dogs gallop around a circle track. But if he is trialled or allowed to gallop with a dog of his own age, over a short distance on a straight run or track, there should be no risk of injury to him. In fact, it would be helpful in his education. Be sure the dog is on a calcium supplement such as Calci-D, and also limit galloping to short hand slips and short trials over 200 yards or so.

2. Q I had a bit of a bonus recently. As I was about to put my little bitch into the car to go racing, she slipped her lead and dashed up the field after something that had caught her eye. I caught her after about five minutes, but I was a bit worried about her spending so much energy before she raced and so I didn't back her. It was just my hard luck, because she took off and did her fastest ever run at the track.

My mate wasn't too surprised. He said he always gives his dogs a gallop on the day of a race. Was it just luck, or is there any physical reason why a dog would run well on a day that he has already had a gallop?

A A short hand slip over 200-300 yards, followed by a warm-down walk for five minutes on the lead often helps to improve a greyhound's interest and race-ready condition.

I know of greyhounds that are sprinted up the track an hour or so before racing, and come out straining on the lead to race and win. Stud dogs can even be used on race day and then win races 6-8 hours later.

A short sprint on race day certainly does not hurt, but obviously in hot weather or over longer distances to travel to race, you should assess the greyhound's overall condition.

Saplings need free-running exercise while they are growing. This can be stepped up to short hand-slips as the greyhounds mature.

Top trainer George Curtis takes a string of greyhounds for early morning exercise. A short sprint on a race day will not harm a greyhound, as long as it is not too hot.

3. Q Could you please help solve an argument between a friend and myself concerning the use of anabolic steroids. Many years ago I was told by a very good vet that anabolic steroids could not make a dog run any faster than he was capable of; they merely speeded up the process to get him into tip-top condition.

My friend insists that many of the top trainers use these drugs regularly without being detected and that these steroids can improve performance, as with Ben Johnson. More recently, I see there is a strong school of thought in athletics that admits they put on bulk but refutes the idea that they improve performance, even in the power sports.

David Jenkins (the former British athlete, who was convicted of importing anabolic steroids) has admitted that his performance suffered once he started using them. To sum up, is there any proof that these drugs really do enhance performance in any animal?

A There is little evidence that anabolic steroids increase the all-out speed of a greyhound. In fact, it can actually have the reverse effect by increasing bulk but not the speed. This often happens in the larger dogs where anabolic steroids can help strengthen and build muscle in response to exercise. In many cases, the greyhound becomes excessively bulky and heavy, thus increasing the risk of damage to toes and muscles due to the heavier bodyweight, and actually slows down in performance. However, whilst the endurance to run over distance is enhanced, the bulk and muscle mass reduces all-out top speed.

Anabolic steroids are widely used, and are reported to have benefit in sports requiring muscle bulk but not speed, but it appears to have little or no benefit in athletic animals. Obviously, the use of anabolic steroids to build up muscle strength and power is useful, but in many athletes speed is sacrificed for excessive muscle bulk. However, in horse sports requiring endurance, anabolic steroids accordingly increase endurance and stamina of the animal to compete over longer distances. In racing horses they are also used by many trainers to increase the 'confidence' and competitiveness of the horse in gruelling equestrian sports. However, various studies have failed to support their use in increasing ability in race horses per se.

Certainly, oral anabolic steroids in racing greyhounds may help to build up body muscle when combined with adequate exercise and also give timid animals more 'confidence' for competition. They are also reported to be beneficial in stimulating red blood cell production, and helping to maintain adequate red cell count during training. Again, this is probably more allied to the horse rather than the racing greyhound.

To sum up, there is no real evidence that anabolic steroids actually enhance the performance of an animal. Although anabolic courses will help to increase the rate of development of an animal, when combined with exercise, their use for this benefit would be confined to the earlier training period. Dosage with strong 'male' hormones to greyhound dogs can sometimes increase their aggression to the stage where they might 'turn their head' or fight during trialling.

KENNELS

4. Q I am thinking of buying a new kennel. It was previously used for rearing Irish Setters. Is there anything that I can do to the land to kill off any bugs or infections before I put my greyhounds on to it? Ultimately, I would like to breed a few litters.

A It is a good idea to thoroughly wash out and scrub the kennel area with a suitable disinfectant solution, and rinse off any residues. Special wash preparations, such as Parvocide, are available from your veterinary surgeon which are formulated to destroy parvovirus and other bacterial and viral diseases, when applied as directed. You can also hire a steam cleaner to heat sterilise and clean the floors and walls under pressure, rather than elbow grease and scrubbing.

The cleaning of the outside yards is not as easy, but raking over lightly contaminated areas and spraying with Parvocide-type preparations is helpful. However, if the runs are 'sour' and smelly, and are at risk of containing heavy hookworm contamination, then the only effective way is to call in a machine to dig out and replace the contaminated soil to a depth of six inches or so, and replace it with clean fill. Broadcasting lime around yards is not effective, and may actually slow the natural soil decomposing mechanisms.

I suggest you have your own veterinary surgeon inspect the land with you, to give specific advice on the needs and methods to decontaminate the area. It may be cheaper in the long term to get specific professional advice before you decide to purchase the area, particularly before you commence to shift tons of soil, etc. in an effort to reduce worm and disease build-up.

TRAINER'S TIP

At least twice daily collection of stools in puppy runs is an important part of long-term worm control by breeders. Hookworm infestation in particular, can build up and contaminate the soil profile and in heavily stocked runs in continuous use, it is best to remove the top layer of soil to a depth of 15cm (6") at least and replace with fresh soil at intervals of two years, or if stool egg counts increase to high levels despite a rigorous worming programme.

CONTAGIOUS DISEASES/VACCINATIONS

5.Q **Many greyhound trainers suffer loss of income through kennel cough. Is there any preventative feeding or kennel routine that can minimise the chances of a dog going down with the cough? This is a problem for a trainer like me who is limited for space.**
What type of feeding would you recommend to speed up the recovery process, and so cut the risk of the cough hitting the whole kennel?

A Obviously vaccination against kennel cough is probably the most effective means of preventing the initial infection. However, once kennel cough spreads in a kennel of greyhounds, then any infected dogs should be quarantined in a separate area of the kennel. All affected dogs should be shifted to one end of the kennel, and be fed separately. Their kennel area should be treated with a wash that has action against viruses, such as Parvocide Wash, and their food bowls, etc. washed in hot water after other bowls in the kennel have been cleaned.

As far as feeding is concerned, then certain vitamins such as vitamin E, as contained in White-E, and vitamins A and C have been shown to be useful in helping to increase the immune response against various viral diseases. Doses of vitamin A of about 6000iu daily, doses of vitamin E of about 200iu a day, and up to 1000mg of vitamin C a day for a week or so may be helpful in improving response to vaccination and also helping to increase immunity against viral and other diseases.

As far as medication is concerned, this is a job for your vet. Generally, cough syrups are helpful in relieving the irritant cough. Nebulising airway dilating drugs and antibiotics, with a face mask,

Kennels and yards should be thoroughly disinfected and kept clean at all times to minimise the risk of infection.

is useful in severe infections. Unfortunately, the infectious germs can be shed by dogs prior to showing symptoms of kennel cough. Also the persistence of the germ in the environment adds to the difficulty in cleaning the infected premises. The humidity in some kennels also increases risk of spread in the environment, and an uptake of any virus germs that could trigger the development of the kennel cough complex.

Q **Recently my bitch had a litter of eight pups. I had them injected against parvovirus and the other ailments. Then only a week after the second injection, five of them took ill. Two later died with what was proved to be parvovirus. Please enlighten me on the after-effects of the virus on pups intended for racing.** **6.**

A I am afraid your story is not unusual. Parvovirus is still with us and still causing losses, even though we have better vaccines these days. If the bitch has been vaccinated against parvovirus or has recovered from it, she will pass on a passive immunity to her puppies. This will protect them for the first few weeks of life but the immunity will gradually wane.

Unfortunately, this immunity will also interfere with the vaccine. Puppies are normally vaccinated at eight, twelve and twenty weeks. It is possible for the immunity acquired from the bitch to interfere with either the eight-week, or even the twelve-week injection, but then wane, so that the pup becomes susceptible to infection before the next and presumably, potentially effective injection, so that the pup is ill even though vaccinated.

The effect of parvovirus on recovered racing greyhound whelps is variable. If the pups are under one month old then the probability is that their hearts will be affected and they will be useless for racing. Fortunately, nowadays this early infection is rare due to the protection derived from the vaccinated dam. Pups contracting parvovirus at a later age usually make a complete recovery, provided that the symptoms are promptly treated and severe diarrhoea and dehydration are prevented.

Q **I have a three-month-old litter of pups who appeared quite healthy until recently. One morning, I discovered that one of the pups had one eye that was a milky colour. The following day, a second pup developed the same condition and both pups appeared blind in the 'milky' eye. My local vet gave me some Opticlox ointment, and the second pup appears to have recovered completely after a week's treatment.** **7.**

The condition of the first pup seems to have improved, although it has still not cleared up properly. Can you give me some idea on what has caused the problem? The pups had received their inoculations about three weeks prior to the eye problems, though I do not know whether this is significant.

A Some years ago it was not uncommon for young puppies to develop a syndrome called 'blue eye' or 'milky eye' following their inoculations with vaccines for protection against canine hepatitis virus. Occasionally, some greyhounds will still develop the 'blue eye' syndrome, despite very well purified vaccines.

I would suggest that you talk to your vet regarding the vaccine used, and then contact the manufacturer of the vaccine for their comment on whether they have had similar problems with the inoculation. In most cases the eyes will tend to clear up after a period of two to four weeks, and you should make sure your veterinarian supervises their treatment with antibiotics and any other medications necessary.

The only other condition that would cause 'milky eye' would be a low grade infection in the eye, possibly due to a dirty kennel environment. In this case, make sure your kennels are clean, and again consult your veterinary surgeon for more detailed recommendations.

SKIN PROBLEMS

8. Q **One of my dogs recently developed eczema and despite treating him with an ointment, recommended by my vet, he has failed to recover from it. In fact, it has spread and is now in his ears. Could you recommend suitable treatment?**

Could you also tell me just how contagious eczema is and how one should go about preventing and eliminating it from a kennel.

A Unfortunately, there are many causes of eczema in greyhounds. The most common cause is high infestations of fleas in a sensitive greyhound. This normally causes development of skin irritation with inflammation and itchiness over the rear end of the greyhound above the tail area.

The spread of eczema from around the head and face area, including the ears, is probably most likely due to skin mites, and these should be diagnosed by skin scrapings carried out by your vet. These require treatment with insecticidal type washes, rather than simple ointments. Lastly, eczema can sometimes be caused by environmental factors such as sensitivity to detergents used to clean the kennels, food allergies – particularly red meat allergy – which can cause diarrhoea as well, and also immune-type reactions that can cause certain skin diseases.

Since your greyhound has not responded to an ointment, particularly if it was a cortisone-based ointment, then it is more likely due to fleas, mites or some type of internal allergic reaction. Obviously if the eczema is due to mites or fleas, then it is more easily spread from dog to dog. However, where a dog has an individual sensitivity to environmental factors, then it is unlikely to spread to other dogs.

Generally, good kennel hygiene, including regular change of bedding, and quarantining the affected dog is probably the best way to prevent spread to other greyhounds in the kennels. In some cases, where the cause of the problem cannot be fully diagnosed, then nutritional supplementation with fats and vitamins, such as contained in EfaVet capsules, can be useful. Products such as Feramo-Greyhound, containing a balanced level of vitamins and minerals, can also be useful in ensuring a good healthy coat and correcting minor skin itches and irritations.

9. Q **Can you please recommend a good treatment for mild scurf. I understand that using a substance like olive oil can cause problems with bacteria.**

A It depends on the severity and cause of the scurf build-up in the coat. Greyhounds shed skin on a continuous basis, and in many black-coated greyhounds the particles of scurf appear to be more prominent. A good quality shampoo will help to remove the scurf and condition the skin. Many of the medicated shampoos used for human scalp conditions are useful in greyhounds, provided they do not excessively dry the coat.

In some cases a selenium based shampoo, available from your vet, will be recommended if the dog is also scratching himself excessively. In severe scurfy coats, where the dog is itching and scratching, particularly during the summer months, then you should ensure that you have an adequate flea control programme. I suggest that you consult your own vet regarding the best form of flea control in your kennels.

However, where the coat is dry and dull with excessive scurf, then a fatty acid supplement such as EfaVet 1 would be beneficial to overcome the initial scurfy problem, particularly in older retired greyhounds. A supplement then of polyunsaturated cooking oils, or in severe cases a product such as EfaVet Regular capsules, would be recommended. These will help to improve the coat condition and reduce the amount of skin shed in otherwise healthy dogs.

Generally, substances like olive oil can create a film of oil on the skin under which bacteria can multiply, as well as increase the risk of oil in the kennels and attracting dust and dirt to the coat. I would suggest that you shampoo the greyhound a couple of times with a coal tar based shampoo or a selenium based shampoo, and if the scurf still remains excessive, then I would consult your vet for a more detailed diagnosis.

TRAINER'S TIP

Ideally greyhounds should receive a diet containing 12-15 per cent fat, such as provided by lean to medium fat beef. Other meats, such as horse, lean chicken, and fish often contain less than optimum fat levels for digestion and performance. One tablespoon of lard, meat trimming fat, suet, or even polyunsaturated vegetable oil per 350g of lean meat will help boost fat intake. In addition to normal dietary fat, 2 teaspoons (half a tablespoon) of polyunsaturated vegetable oil added daily to the diet will help promote a healthy, well conditioned skin and hair coat in a racing greyhound. Particularly useful for black coated greyhounds with a 'scurfy' and dull coat.

10. Q I am writing to enquire whether there is any treatment which I can give to my greyhound which has dandruff. He is a black dog which, after massage, is covered in dandruff. He is racing and is fit. For the past three months I have given him tonics and vitamins along with a daily dose of cod-liver oil. His coat blooms, but the dandruff is persisting all over the dog's body. I hope that you can give me advice to clear the problem.

A It is not uncommon for black greyhounds, such as your dog, to appear to have a larger amount of dandruff in their coat than other coloured greyhounds. This is because it is more easily contrasted to their hair coat colour, and thus more obvious to the owner.

The tonics, vitamins and cod-liver oil should help to provide the necessary minerals and vitamins that your dog requires for his coat condition. In many cases, regular brushing out of the coat in such a dog will help to remove excess dandruff and eventually reduce the total amount of flaky skin that is lost.

The condition could be considered a type of dermatitis, or inflammation of the skin, if it appears to be causing itchiness or the dog scratches and rubs himself more than normal. In that case I would suggest you take him to your own veterinary surgeon for an examination of his skin. A product such as Seleen, available from your veterinary surgeon, may be useful to overcome low grade dermatitis and reduce the flaking of the skin. However, you may need to wash the dog two or three times over a period of two weeks or so, to obtain the best results.

Heavy flea burdens on a dog may increase the level of flaky skin, resulting in the build-up of

TRAINER'S TIP

When adding tablets with an unfamiliar odour to the meal (such as Methnine 90 tablets as illustrated), place the tablets onto the meat proportion of the diet, and push into the mince with the fingers. Let stand for 2-3 minutes to allow the tablet to absorb the meat "juice" and taste before feeding. Alternatively, pop tablets over the tongue just prior to feeding, or wrap in a cheese "sausage" as illustrated in the Trainer's Tip on page 16.

dandruff. In these cases you would need to regularly treat the dog for fleas as recommended by your veterinary surgeon.

Many black dogs tend to suffer from chronic types of dehydration. This highlights the dryness of the skin and makes them appear to be suffering from excessive dandruff. It would be beneficial to add an electrolyte replacer, such as Betacel, to his diet daily to help to overcome the dehydration.

Q Please could you give me some idea how I could prevent and get rid of the white scurf **11.** that my greyhound has? The dog is brushed every day and when bathed is washed with anti-scurf shampoo. As the dog is black, the scurf is very prominent in her fur. She is eight years old and is fed on tripe, biscuits and vitamin supplement.

A It is not uncommon for scurf to be common in the black-coated older dog. Although brushing and washing with a cleaning shampoo will help to remove some of the scurf, recent studies have suggested that it could be due to a lack of an essential oil in the diet.

Although you are currently feeding a vitamin supplement, this may not contain the correct balance of vitamins and oils required in the older dog. A deficiency of an essential oil in the diet leads to increased shedding of the skin layers, dryness and wrinkling of the skin. Addition of 2 tsp of polyunsaturated vegetable oil and 1/4 tsp of cod-liver oil will provide essential fatty acids and vitamins to maintain good coat and skin condition.

TRAINER'S TIP

When giving tablets to a puppy, or a greyhound that resists administration over the tongue, simply wrap the tablet in a couple of layers of soft cheese slice, and pop the cheesy "sausage" into the eagerly awaiting open mouth. This method is particularly useful for coated tablets, such as slow release potassium (eg. Beta-K), which should not be crunched up as can occur if they are mixed with food.

WORMING

12. Q   **I worm my dogs every six months. Last time I used those all-in-one tablets and one of the dogs was violently sick and had an upset stomach. Was it the tablets? How successful are they?**

A   It is certainly a wise precaution to worm greyhounds regularly, especially when young. I hope you will also try to control the problem by attention to the environment. This means that stools should be picked up daily from the paddocks and all damp dark places in which worm eggs can survive. Grass should be cut down and care should be taken to ensure good drainage, particularly in wet weather. It is also important to remember that however efficient your worming procedures are, they have no residual effect. When the worms have been removed new ones re-colonise your dog's bowels.

You do not say which product you have used, but from your description it may be Lopatol. It is highly effective in a single dose against a number of parasites. The dose is 1 x 500mg per 10 kg/22 lb bodyweight. The tablets are film-coated and should not be broken. They are administered orally and should be given whole.

For the best results, the tablets should be given together with a small quantity of food on an empty stomach. The dog should then be starved for eight hours. They do make some dogs vomit, but apparently this does not affect their efficiency.

DIGESTION

13. Q   **I have always cleaned out all my dogs on a regular basis by using washing soda. I understand that there is an injection that my vet could give a dog to do the same job. Could you please tell me a) what is it called, b) does it work better than crystals, and c) are there are side effects?**

A   Over the years, a dose of washing soda has been a popular method to stimulate a greyhound to vomit bile. A preparation called Apomorphine is used by veterinary surgeons to stimulate dogs to vomit in the case of poisonings, and this is also used to clean out racing greyhounds. This preparation administered by injection, or as a small tablet under the eyelid, stimulates the greyhound to vomit in about seven to ten minutes. Trainers feed a light meal of bread and milk just beforehand, so the animal has something to bring up rather than dry retching, which is distressing to the animal. The side effects are minimal, but some animals may experience discomfort if they have little to vomit or the effect persists for longer than normal.

Other preparations, such as mild laxatives (e.g. Bilex for greyhounds), are becoming more popular, as they gently clean the animal out through the bowels without the discomfort of vomiting. Preparations such as Bilex are used on a regular weekly or fortnightly basis to keep the bowels in good condition. If you wish to continue to vomit bile your greyhounds, then discuss the options with your own veterinary surgeon for advice in the particular need of your greyhounds.

14. Q   **I purchased a greyhound dog with two recent trials on his Irish card. He led in his trial at the sale but finished badly with cramp. I am not worried about that. I have put him on Seavit tablets to help him with the cramp. But every time I feed the dog, up comes his food, five minutes later, with white slime. I have tried him on dried and wet food,**

but the same thing happens. I have kept greyhounds for fifty years, but I have never had one who vomits as soon as you feed him. I have now wormed him, but I have not trialled him as I thought I would give him time to settle down. Any suggestions you make would be appreciated. I have just found out that this dog had been ill some time before the sale – how bad he was, I do not know.

A Your greyhound certainly presents a problem. You do not have a full background on the dog's previous history, although you have found out that it had been ill for some time prior to the sale.

In most cases where a dog vomits food soon after eating, it is associated with a blockage in the bowel or a stomach infection. The greyhound may have eaten a plastic bag, plastic twine, bedding or other indigestible object that could be limiting the size of his stomach and causing him to vomit after feeding. In this case the dog would be losing weight and would certainly have a bigger risk of cramping in his races due to an electrolyte loss from vomiting.

It appears from your description that your dog is most likely to have a gastritis or inflammation of the stomach, which would explain the white slime brought up after vomiting. I would suggest that you take the dog to your local vet for a thorough examination, particularly since you have only had him for the last week or so. Severe worm infestations can also cause vomiting and blockage of the bowel. But in any case, I think you should seek advice from your vet. I certainly would recommend that you do not trial him until you have him examined by a vet.

Q My dog has problems with bad breath and occasionally vomits himself. I have checked his teeth which are all OK, and his saliva is clear. Basically, it is just a very 'doggy' smell, nothing unusual. **15.**

A friend recently drew my attention to an entry in a veterinary encyclopedia which stated that dogs do not cope easily with cow's milk. I intend to experiment by cutting out cow's milk in his breakfast. I would be interested to know, though, whether you reckon it would adversely affect his digestion.

A Obviously your greyhound is suffering from some low grade gut irritation that either causes bad breath, or stimulates him to vomit himself. It is probably best to have your greyhound thoroughly checked out by a veterinary surgeon.

Although some greyhounds tend to react to milk, generally it is in the form of allergy type symptoms, with skin itching and in most cases increased looseness of their bowels. If the cow's milk is high in fat then this could upset his stomach, and therefore it would be worth reducing it and seeing if that makes any difference.

Some greyhounds are sensitive to red meat in their diets, and this can lead to low grade diarrhoea and a 'foul' smelling breath. If you are feeding red meat, it may be worth changing to chicken or fish for a week or so, to see whether that helps his digestion. If the dog does not suffer from diarrhoea on a regular basis, then again it is unlikely to be a red meat allergy. In some cases feeding your greyhound on dry food and rice for a week could help to relieve any gastric upsets.

With regard to his teeth, even though the teeth themselves may appear to be clean, bacteria that cause bad breath can build up around the teeth/gum margins. In this case it would be best to swab the teeth/gum margins with a cotton-bud dipped in 50/50 hydrogen peroxide and water. This can be repeated daily for two or three days, and this will kill off the harmful bacteria that lead to bad breath. In some cases, greyhounds that have 'tartar' on their teeth that harbour bacteria, also have inflamed tonsils. It would also be important to ensure that the greyhound is not eating his own manure. I would suggest that you try the above dietary changes and, should this fail to resolve the problem, then have your dog thoroughly examined by your veterinary surgeon.

COAT CARE

16. Q **My three-year-old greyhound bitch displays a lack of hair growth, and has done since we first got her 18 months ago. She is bald on the hindquarters, elbows, chest and underbelly, and behind the ears. The condition is worsening. She is a regular visitor to the vet, and recent blood samples showed the thyroid and progesterone to be in order. The vet is happy with the diet and vitamins she is given, but he says her body metabolism may not be using what she is given properly.**

Apart from her baldness, she is physically well-proportioned, maintains a good weight and appears happy with her environment. The bitch should come into season this month, making it one full year since her last break. She is virtually unraced because her times deteriorated from top-class to poor grading. The lack of hair growth seems to be at the root of the problem. Can this be rectified?

A It is not uncommon for greyhounds to develop what is called 'bald thigh syndrome' when in training. Usually the hair starts to fall out about four weeks after entering a full training programme, and there is a progressive loss of hair from the sides of each thigh in particular. The hair in the area behind the shoulders and under the chest may also thin and develop a 'bald' type appearance.

In early cases, greyhounds do not show any signs of illness. There is a progressive loss of hair along the thighs, but it does not worry the dog in any way. In most cases it is thought to be due to a thyroid hormone deficiency, but since the thyroid function has been shown to be in order in your bitch, then there may be some other reason for it. Sometimes, very abrasive floors in the kennel and sleeping on rough bags can cause loss of hair, particularly on the thighs as the greyhound gets up from rest.

Your bitch certainly shows the common loss of performance associated with the more chronic condition, and many greyhounds become erratic in their racing, and lose concentration and tend to run places instead of winning. There are a couple of treatments, but these must be administered by your vet.

The first one is an injection of a hormone called Acth which can be of use, particularly during a stressful racing period. Your vet would need to administer this drug and also monitor it to ensure that the greyhound is not receiving excessive amounts. The use of anabolic steroids is commonly used in many countries to help reduce the dehydration and loss of bodyweight associated with the condition. However, you would need to talk to your vet prior to administering any type of anabolic to your racing greyhound. In many cases, although thyroid function appears to be normal on a blood test, the administration of a low dose of thyroid hormone may be beneficial. Again, this would need to be carried out by your vet.

The dry coat can be improved by feeding a supplement such as EfaVet 1 tablets, which contain fats and vitamins which improve coat condition. The dehydration can be overcome by giving a product such as Betacel electrolyte replacer, to provide extra potassium and other body salts.

It is also helpful to change the training programme to reduce stress on the greyhound. It is best to reduce walking to about one mile a day, and give one hand slip over 250 yards once or twice a week. Avoid racing the greyhound more frequently than 10-14 days apart, and try to keep the bitch physically fit with small hand slips over 200 yards, rather than giving her hard trials.

Q **I have a retired four-year-old greyhound, and I have had him for a year. He is in fine condition, but he has a bare patch near the top of his tail, and also the fur on his thighs is not as thick as on the rest of him. My vet tells me that certain breeds are susceptible to the tail problem and it is to do with the glands.**

17.

I have tried Oxydex shampoo, and he has a supplement of Pet-Coat every day. The condition has developed over the last six months. He lives indoors in a fully carpeted house and has a thick foam-bed covered with a blanket. He is fed on brown bread and minced chicken or fish, and he has plenty of exercise. There appears to be no irritation as the condition does not trouble the dog, but I do take him to shows, so would be very grateful if you could give me any advice.

A It is not uncommon for greyhounds to develop this type of bald patch, particularly under the stress of hard work. In most cases, the hair growth returns to normal once the dog is retired. However, treatment with a tablet that contains the thyroid hormone, thyroxine, has been found to be useful in treating bald thigh syndrome in racing greyhounds. Your vet would be able to give you more specific advice on the use of these tablets.

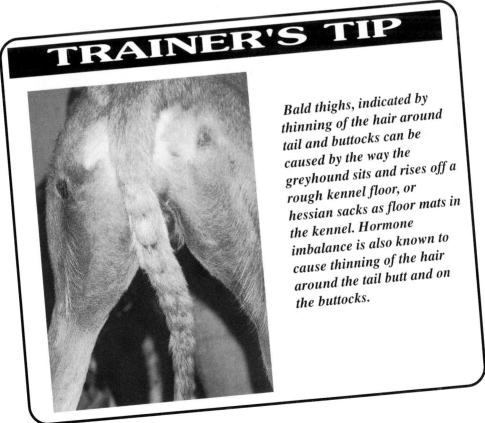

TRAINER'S TIP

Bald thighs, indicated by thinning of the hair around tail and buttocks can be caused by the way the greyhound sits and rises off a rough kennel floor, or hessian sacks as floor mats in the kennel. Hormone imbalance is also known to cause thinning of the hair around the tail butt and on the buttocks.

A relatively new product called EfaVet 1, which contains essential fatty acids and vitamins, is also useful in treating various inflammatory and stress-related skin conditions in dogs. Usually about four weeks of supplementation with EfaVet capsules is required to give the best results. Where the skin is dry it may also be useful to rub in a moisturising ointment containing vitamin A.

Chronic flea irritation can cause bald patches on the rump above the tail base, but this is usually itchy and you will notice the greyhound rubbing. At times acrylic carpets can also be abrasive, and if the greyhound sits down and wags his tail a lot, the hair loss will occur on the tail and on the sides of the hindquarters as he pivots to stand up. Perhaps you could provide him with a softer mat or rug if he has a favourite spot where he sits on the carpet.

Vitamin A appears to be useful in revitalising the skin and hair growth. Both chicken and fish are low in essential minerals such as iron and copper, which are also required for the health of the skin. However, the supplement of Pet-Coat every day that you are currently giving should provide some of these minerals. Alternatively, a supplement such as Feramo-Greyhound, which is specially designed for racing greyhounds, could be useful in providing other essential minerals and vitamins.

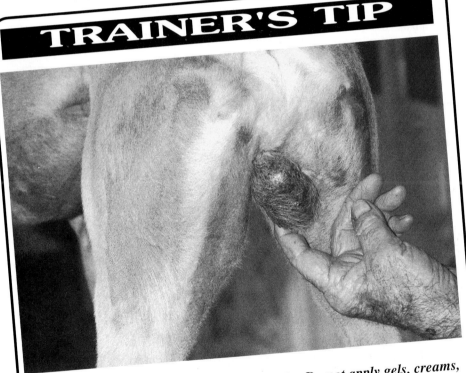

TRAINER'S TIP

Testicles can be chafed by sand on dry tracks. Do not apply gels, creams, or petroleum jelly as it collects sand. Sprinkle the testicles and inside of legs with dry baby powder before galloping to prevent chaffing and pinching.

Q **I recently purchased a greyhound, who is two years old. He is a big dog and looks very** **18.**
well except for a loss of fur on the back end and on the back of his tail. He was bedded
on straw. I have had him bedded on paper for the last three months, but there is only
a marginal difference. I have just started rubbing antiseptic cream on nightly.

A Many greyhounds under the stress of repeated racing and training lose hair over the thighs
and tail area. This is thought to be due to loss of hair caused by a thyroid deficiency, which
prevents normal hair re-growth. In these cases, the skin is usually fairly shiny, and there is
no evidence of fine hair on the skin. A course of Thyroxine tablets from your vet may be useful in
overcoming this type of bald thigh problem. However, if the coat is dry and there is some evidence
of more hairs attempting to re-grow, then in most cases this is simply due to the dog wearing the
hair off on the bedding.

Although shredded paper bedding is usually useful in correcting these conditions, you have had
disappointing results. I would suggest that you construct a hammock-type bed out of an old sack,
so that the dog lies in the bed without contact with the floor. Hammock beds are also useful to
control fleas, and they are easier to clean and maintain than conventional bedding materials. Some
dogs dig down into the bedding and rub their backsides and tails on the abrasive surface of the

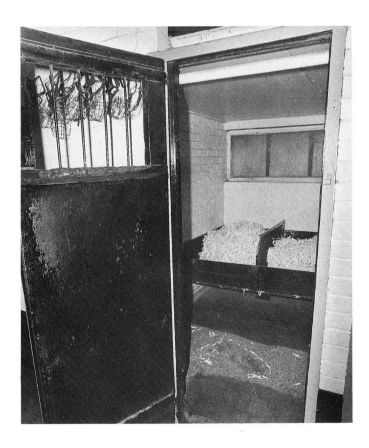

*Shredded paper
bedding can be used
for greyhounds who
are suffering from
hair-loss. It is
important that the
bedding is kept clean
and dry at all times.*

underlying floor. If the skin is very dry and flaky, then a mineral and vitamin supplement such as Feramo-D may be helpful in providing extra vitamins to help balance the diet. Also, adding 10-12ml of polyunsaturated oil each day to the diet is useful in preventing dry skin conditions. This type of condition is most common in greyhounds fed very lean meat without added fat to the diet.

The only other possibility, of course, would be a problem with fleas. Some dogs develop an allergy to fleas and will lose patches of hair on the thighs and on the butt of the tail. Therefore, regular treatment to control fleas would be appropriate in this case. Your vet would be able to give you more specific advice as to whether fleas could be the underlying cause. Remember, when controlling fleas it is important to thoroughly treat the kennel area to reduce the level of re-contamination with fleas and flea eggs.

19. Q **Could you tell me what causes hair to come off in the middle of my bitch's tail? Is there anything I can get to restore it?**

A If the bitch does not attempt to bite the area and it does not appear to irritate her, then it may be simply due to knocking her tail whilst wagging it and moving around her kennel. Quite often greyhounds put their tails under the edge of a bed, and this can cause hair loss as the dog moves around or wags its tail.

In this case, a light smear of an ointment containing vitamin A, such as Morsep, would be recommended. This will help clear up any low grade infection in the skin and allow the hair to grow back. If you think the bitch is rubbing her tail, then I suggest that you put a light gauze bandage over the area to help her avoid her abrasing her skin as she rubs her tail.

20. Q **I am thirteen years old, and I have been going greyhound racing for two years now. I have a brindle bitch, called Bonnie, and she is two years old. I race her mostly once a week. She is as fit as a fiddle, I think I do all the things right, which my dad tells me. But there's one thing I can't get right, and that is that her coat does not keep its shine. It seems to go dull very quickly. So please could you give me some advice on what to do. The other thing with Bonnie is that sometimes she runs a great race, and other times she just seems to not want to run.**

A There are lots of reasons why a greyhound might have a dull coat. In most cases it is due to either worms or dehydration. However, if you have wormed the dog regularly and the coat is elastic and springs back after being pinched up, then there may be some other reason for the dullness.

Some greyhounds have a naturally dull coat, but, in most cases, a supplement of vitamins and minerals will help to improve the dog's general health, and increase the lustre of the coat. A daily supplement such as Feramo-Greyhound would be beneficial to provide minerals such as iron and zinc, and vitamins such as A and B complex, which normally help to improve coat condition.

A daily dose of polyunsaturated oil, such as 2 tsp of blended cooking oil, provides extra oil to condition the skin and hair. It is also beneficial to brush the dog regularly each day to stimulate the release of natural oils from the hair follicles. This should help to give your greyhound a shiny coat.

As regards the occasional loss of interest in racing, then this could be due to stress or tiredness from regular racing or travelling. Some greyhounds do not race well under cold conditions; other fail to chase at night, etc. If you are concerned, have Bonnie checked by your vet.

BITES

Q One of my dogs received a nasty bite from another of my greyhounds when they were **21.**
out exercising. I bathed it in warm water and TCP, and it appears to be healing OK.
It was certainly not bad enough to call out the vet, but I wondered if there was any
treatment you would recommend for these sorts of cases?

A Dog bites are almost inevitable when several animals are kept together. Continual
vigilance, securely fastened collars and leads, and a sensible approach to those known to be
of uncertain temperament can help to avoid such eventualities. But most owners will have
to deal with a dog bite sooner or later.

Dog bites vary considerably in severity from a surface skin wound to severe tissue damage that
may even result in death. Some bites may be deep and penetrating and present a fairly small
surface wound. These are usually quite painful and can prove difficult. Often skin or hair is driven
deep into the wound and until removed the wound will not heal.

In some cases the wound heals over, but an abscess forms. Deep wounds can be complicated by
severe infections, blood poisoning or septicaemia and severe pain, collapse and death. Bites of this
type need cleaning, fomenting and keeping open in order to drain any pus that forms. An antibiotic
cover is almost essential in severe cases, by injection given by your vet.

When cleaning, the hair should first be clipped away for about one inch all round the wound.
Warm water and soap are useful in the first instance, and, in fact, soap itself is a good antiseptic.
Fomentation should be hot and should be continued for at least 10 minutes twice a day. A small
bucket should be half-filled with hot water with some disinfectant, e.g. Dettol, TCP, Cetavlon or
similar. A piece of cotton wool should be soaked in the water, the excess allowed to drain away
and the hot pad held against the wound until it has cooled. This should then be repeated. The
object is to apply heat and a certain amount of massage to the wound.

Those bites involving greater skin damage are usually more superficial. The skin will be torn
and the flap may be detached or turned inwards. The underlying tissue may also be involved.
Unless the wound is very superficial, veterinary attention should be sought. Once again,
cleanliness is most important. Clean the wound, clip it and apply wound powder and, if possible, a
bandage. Make certain the skin is in the correct position.

NASAL PROBLEMS

Q I have a brindle hound dog – two years old – which I bought six months ago. His nose **22.**
runs with clear water and the dog is constantly licking it. When out walking he makes
a snorting noise, similar to a head cold. He has been wormed and had a course of
antibiotics. The dog is in first-class condition and is running well apart from this. Have you
any suggestions on how to clear this up?

A It is very uncommon to have a greyhound with a persistent nasal drip. From your
description the dog appears to be healthy in every way, and is performing well, and
therefore it is unlikely to be something that is affecting his nasal system.

It is not uncommon for greyhounds to develop allergies to dust in the environment and bedding.
Dust mites, in particular, can cause runny nose and asthma-like symptoms, and in bad cases this
would affect his performance. Therefore, if the bedding is dusty, then change to a less dusty type

of material, such as shredded paper. An allergic type response to dust or other irritants in the environment could be reduced by giving the dog a short course of an antihistamine or similar product that would reduce inflammation in his nasal area and may reduce the secretion of fluid. Therefore, I would suggest that you talk to your vet about giving the dog a course of nasal decongestant to dry up his runny nose. This may need to be done on a trial basis, to see if it clears up for a period of time.

I assume also that your greyhound has been thoroughly examined by your vet. It may be that he has an irritation in his nasal cavity, such as a small cancer, which could be irritating the nasal membranes and increasing the secretion of fluid. The snorting noise that he makes does suggest that there could be something blocking his airflow when walking. However, if it was bad enough, the dog would drop away in performance.

23. Q **I have a two-year-old greyhound bitch, and last year her nose became completely dried up and crusty. I took her to two vets, but to no avail. I want to know if there is anything I could do for it?**

One vet said it was lack of vitamins so he gave her a course of them. The nose became a little moist, but dried up and became crusty a week later. I wonder if you would know what it is and how to treat it? I don't think the bitch is completely healthy, even though she has no other complaints and is in good form.

A Many trainers, and dog owners in general, believe that an outward sign of health in a dog is a wet nose. This is true in many cases, but dogs with a regularly dry nose can still be healthy and fit for racing. Since your bitch appears healthy and has good form, then it is probably nothing to be unduly concerned about.

Occasionally, greyhounds develop a drier than normal nose when they are chronically dehydrated, with signs such as dry skin, harsh coat, and the skin pinches up. Because they have less fluid in their body they tend not to lick their nose as often. Addition of electrolytes or body salts, e.g. body replacers such as Betacel, may help to correct this problem.

More commonly, greyhounds that have had a cold or cough due to certain virus diseases, e.g. distemper ('hard pad' disease), can develop permanent thickening of the skin on their nose which appears cracked and dried up. Although deficiency of vitamin A, zinc and some other trace nutrients can cause thickening of the skin, your bitch would probably exhibit poor racing form as well. However, it would be best to keep her on a vitamin tonic recommended by your vet.

If the bitch has a dried yellowish crust around her nose and lips, then it could be due to her licking her vulva as a result of irritation due to breeding tract or urinary problems. If you notice that she is urinating frequently and is licking her vulva, then it would be best to seek advice from your vet.

SALIVARY PROBLEM

24. Q **My greyhound has very large saliva glands. I have had his blood checked and it is all in order. He has just had a course of antibiotics; his glands are still rather large and seem to go bigger, then go smaller, but they do not go down.**

My vet says his saliva ducts are probably blocked and suggests an operation to remove glands. I think this is a bit drastic and would like to know if you could offer any other treatment.

A I assume that the salivary glands on the back of his jaw are enlarged. These are called the parotid salivary glands, and one is located on each side of the head. The build-up of saliva in parotid glands can be due to infection, blockage of the duct, or bruising and injury to the duct as it travels behind the cheek.

If the dog is in good health, there is no need to worry about enlarged glands. This is particularly so in your case where the glands do reduce in size, and only flare up occasionally. However, although the glands can be unblocked where they enter the mouth, in most cases the glands swell again after a short time. Therefore, an operation to take the glands out is considered by most as the most effective way of overcoming the problem.

I would suggest that unless the glands are excessively large, and interfere with the dog's racing muzzle, or are obviously uncomfortable, that you leave well alone.

URINE TESTS

Q **Why do trainers use paper sticks to check on different things in the greyhound's** **25.** **urine. I train my own two greyhound dogs. I took up the sport six years ago, and I have dedicated myself, in every spare minute there is, to try and learn how to bring the best out of these fabulous animals.**

I was invited to a professional kennel, and I asked the trainer what was he checking for when he dipped the paper into the dog's urine. He replied that he was checking for protein levels in the dog. The sticks of paper, however, represented different colour squares on the bottle that he took them out of. Please would you be so kind and give me the information on how to use and what to look for regarding these tests.

A There are various types of urine test sticks available, but from your description it appears to be one that checks for acid levels, protein levels, sugar levels, ketones, bilirubin and blood in the urine. Certainly, the acid level and protein level in the urine are probably the most common ones that are monitored by trainers.

Normally, the greyhound's urine is slightly acid when they are fed on a meat-based diet. However, if the urine becomes alkaline due to lower levels of acid being excreted, or excess alkaline being passed, then this could indicate that there is too much alkaline in the greyhound's diet, or that a low grade infection of the bladder is present.

As regards protein levels, then excessive amounts of protein in the urine can indicate that there is a breakdown of muscle protein after racing. Generally, the protein levels in the urine which relate to the specific gravity of the urine should remain reasonably constant. Any elevation could be an indication of low grade dehydration, excessive muscle damage following exercise, or kidney problems.

As regards the other tests, then it is probably best that you discuss the significance of these with your own vet. The use of test strips can be useful to monitor dogs' urine, but in many cases, a professional interpretation of the results is necessary. Therefore, I would suggest that if you do start to monitor the dogs' urine using the test strips, that you consult your vet should you have any abnormal readings as indicated on the colour changes on the test strips.

Chapter Two

NUTRITION

PREGNANCY/REARING

26. Q One of my brood bitches has recently been mated, and as this is my first litter I want to do what is best for my bitch. However, no-one can give me a straight answer as regards diet.

At the moment I am giving her Respond RS3 for her main meal mixed with chicken, fish and breast of lamb. Breakfast consists of Weetabix, milk and egg.

During the hot weather she went right off her food, but according to all the so-called experts, she is nearly four weeks pregnant, and it is to be expected for her to go off her food at this stage. Now the weather has changed, she still does not have much of an appetite.

I have some friends who train and breed greyhounds, and I have tried the diets they suggest, but my bitch is either fussy, or the food just does not appeal to her. I would also like advice on a suitable diet for the puppies.

A It is not uncommon for a brood bitch in early whelp to go off her feed. You certainly seem to be giving her an adequate and balanced diet. It is helpful sometimes to provide lightly-grilled chicken, beef or lamb, and feed it whilst it is still warm. Feed a mix of one-third meat (250g) and two-thirds dry food (500g) as the evening meal. This often helps to entice a bitch to eat and can be useful in getting them back on their feed.

I would suggest that you cut out excess fatty foods and oil in her diet as this may be causing a nauseating effect that could result in poor appetite. I would also suggest that you put her on to a vitamin/mineral supplement such as Feramo-Greyhound, and perhaps add 2 B-complex vitamin tablets, such as Rebound, every second or third day to generally help her body metabolism and stimulate her appetite.

Over the last three weeks of pregnancy, and once the bitch whelps, increase her diet so that she is getting 50 per cent more at whelping, and a further 50 per cent increase if she has a large litter. You must also ensure that she is being supplemented with adequate calcium such as Dicalcium Phosphate, 2-3 tsp per day mixed in with her evening meal. This will ensure that her unborn puppies have adequate bone growth and development.

As regards a diet for the puppies after weaning, I would suggest the following:

3-4 weeks of age: Once per day – ground beef blended with evaporated milk, and gradually introduce a baby formula vitamin drop.

4-5 weeks: Add a small dry cat biscuit or similar to the above and beat up in the blender, so there are no large lumps of dry biscuit for small pups to contend with – increase to twice a day.

5 weeks onwards: Continue as above once a day, and replace one meal with adult diet, but watch for large pieces, gradually replace the infant formula vitamin drops with a vitamin/mineral supplement.

6 weeks onwards: Increase to 3 meals per day and add calcium supplement, 1 tsp per 10kg bodyweight – I suggest DCP in conjunction with Feramo-Greyhound.

Q **I bought a six-week-old greyhound pup. He is now twelve weeks of age and causing me considerable concern regarding his diet. He is the first puppy I have reared.**
      So far, I have tried him on a few diets which, after a matter of days, he seems to go off – e.g. pet mince and tripe (cooked) with vitalin and brown bread, also raw mince, stewing steak, pig's liver and tripe together with vitalin and brown bread. He also does not seem to like milky meals or lactol.
  The only meal he does like a lot is tripe. I have included this in his meals in an effort to try to tempt him to eat, as he seems to enjoy it so much. But I understand that tripe is not rich enough for a growing pup.

27.

A You certainly seem to have a fussy greyhound pup. Tripe is certainly not rich enough for a growing pup. Tripe contains only 4 per cent protein, 2 per cent fat and has only 1/4 the energy level in the equivalent amount of puppy mince. Therefore, the pup would need to eat a large amount of tripe to get sufficient energy, protein and other nutrients to enable him to grow and develop. However, a small amount of tripe can be used to flavour the meal as you have done. In most cases, greyhound pups like meaty stews and mince meat mixed with biscuit.

I will outline a diet which I have found to be successful in rearing greyhound pups. The amounts recommended are for individual pups ranging from 6 weeks to 12 months of age. The amounts need to be increased within the range as the pup grows and develops.

BREAKFAST: Fresh milk – 1/2-2 cups (reconstituted powdered may also be used), dry dog biscuit – 1/2-1 cup, vitamin E (e.g. White-E) – 50-100iu, calcium powder (DCP 340) – 1 tsp, mix into the milk

LUNCH: 150-250g of 50/50 puppy mince (warmed) with moist biscuit Add gravy or milk if necessary to moisten and flavour. During cold weather the amount may need to be increased by 20 per cent. Alternatively, 50-100g of stewing steak, 50g potatoes, 50g mixed vegetables. Cook for 2-3 hours and then mix with 1/2 cup biscuit. The stew may be flavoured with a beef or chicken flavouring cube.

EVENING MEAL: 150-300g of 50/50 meat and biscuit as for lunch Alternatively, feed a good-quality dry food, about 1-21/2 cups as the pup grows. Moisten with milk or gravy to add taste. Vitamins: e.g. Feramo-Greyhound, 2.4g calcium powder (Dicalcium Phosphate DCP 340) 1/4 tsp extra after 3 months of age; 1 tsp extra after 4 months of age; 11/2 tsp extra after 6 months of age; 2 tsp extra after 8-12 months of age – once the greyhound is sent out for education.

Q **I am rearing two greyhound puppies, now five months old, and I list below the daily amount of food for both. I would like to stop using Canovel tablets and use Biotin Extra instead, the details of which are enclosed along with those of the other tablets and powder I use. However, I would like to know how much to give (since the information is for horses), and if there would be any adverse effects.**

28.

My reason for wanting to use Biotin Extra is to counteract the avidin in the egg whites, which destroys biotin in the intestine. I am a State Registered Nurse, so I have a limited knowledge of the veterinary world.

Feed details (for both dogs, shared meals)

8 a.m. 12 raw eggs, whipped up with 4 pints fresh full-cream cow's milk and 1 tablespoon honey melted in hot water.

4 p.m. 2 lbs Purina soaked in warm water for two hours, with 1/2lb horse meat, 2 tsp of Swift 88 and 1 tsp Calci-D.

8 p.m. 1 pint fresh full-cream milk with 2 tsp Tree Bark powder and 1 tsp honey melted in hot water for each dog.

11 a.m. Butter ball with 3 tsp each of garlic, wheatgerm and mixed vegetable tablets, plus 6 Canovel dog condition tablets.

Two greyhound puppies already reared on the above diet, now 20 months old, are racing exceptionally well, but the present puppies do not like the Canovel.

A Generally, it is most important to ensure that the greyhound pups are kept in a reasonable condition without being excessively heavy, and that they receive adequate exercise to strengthen and develop their muscles.

As regards feeding, the dose of biotin for horses is usually calculated at about 15mg a day as a

TRAINER'S TIP

A treat of chopped mutton flaps or large chunks of brisket bones are helpful in developing the teeth and jaws, relieving boredom and providing extra fat and calcium to improve digestion in young growing puppies. Feed twice weekly in addition to calcium supplements to ensure good bone and skeletal development. A supplement containing Vitamin D is important during the winter months to ensure optimum absorption of supplementary calcium. Select a calcium supplement with added vitamin D, or a general vitamin and mineral supplement containing vitamin D.

treatment for hoof conditions in horses. The exact amount for young greyhounds is unknown, but I would assume that approximately 1/2-1mg a day would be quite adequate to satisfy most needs. Certainly, excessive amounts of egg-white can destroy biotin in the intestine, and therefore possibly double of this amount would be recommended for the younger puppies.

However, I would suggest that you lightly cook the eggs by cracking them into hot water and letting them stand for 30-60 seconds to destroy the biotin. Once the egg-whites start to turn white, most of the avidin that binds up biotin is destroyed. From the description of your diet, you are certainly feeding large amounts of milk, but as long as the greyhounds can tolerate it, milk should provide adequate fluids, some calcium and protein to the diet.

The rest of the diet seems quite adequate for the age of greyhound, but I suggest that you carefully monitor the level of calcium in the diet. The level of calcium in Biotin Extra and that in Calci-D would need to be monitored and increased as the greyhounds develop. Generally, greyhounds should receive about 300mg per kg of bodyweight of calcium per day. Milk contains about 300mg per cupful, and the level of calcium in the dry food would also need to be considered.

However, the success of your older pups probably proves that your dietary balance is adequate, and that these puppies should be reared and fed in a similar way.

TRAINER'S TIP

A daily supplement of calcium is important to balance meat based diets for growing puppies, particularly after weaning. A liquid supplement (e.g. Calci-D Suspension as illustrated) is often recommended to be mixed into the milk feed before weaning, to ensure acceptance in young puppies. This particular calcium suspension is cheese flavoured for addition to milk or meat mince in amounts calculated to balance the calcium to phosphorus ratio relative to the weight of meat provided in the shared puppy diet.

29. Q We recently bought a five-month-old greyhound bitch who was subsequently diagnosed as suffering from colitis. Following a 24-hour fast with only lectade/water mix, we started her on a diet of chicken and boiled rice. The diet and antibiotics prescribed cleared up the problem.

Now we need to improve the diet, but we do not know what she can safely be given so we do not cause a relapse. The vet advocates trial and error. Have you any suggestions please, as we would like to get her to racing standard, despite this setback. She is now seven months old and has put on 12 lbs since we got her; she is very well in herself with plenty of energy.

A The diet you are currently feeding of chicken and boiled rice is prescribed for greyhounds suffering from colitis and diarrhoea. In some cases, the colitis is aggravated by red meat, and therefore the more bland diets are usually helpful in settling down irritation and inflammation in the bowel.

It is also not uncommon for greyhounds to suffer from a 'red meat allergy' that causes low grade diarrhoea and colitis, even when the greyhound is in work and racing. In this case, a change to a chicken and boiled rice diet as you have done, is one of the best ways to manage this type of sensitivity to red meat or what is commonly called 'weak gut syndrome'.

Obviously, the chicken and rice diet will provide plenty of energy and protein for development of your young bitch. In fact, providing you are feeding adequate levels of minerals, particularly iron and other vitamins such as in Feramo-Greyhound and other supplements, then the chicken and rice diet should be quite adequate. However, if you find the diet is rather expensive, then you could reduce the amount of chicken and boiled rice to half, and add either some good-quality dry food or a small amount of red meat.

In most cases, very lean chicken meat can be replaced by about two-thirds of the quantity of lean beef. However, if the chicken meat you are buying is a little bit more fatty, then you can replace beef with the chicken meat on an equal basis. On substitution of dry food for boiled rice, about 1 cup of 20 per cent protein dry food is usually equivalent to about 1 cup boiled rice.

As your vet has advocated, slowly introduce alternative feeds, reducing the chicken and rice accordingly. However, you may wish simply to reduce the boiled rice and replace it with about 20 per cent protein dry food on a substitution rate as outlined above. You could maintain the greyhound on a chicken meat based diet with good quality dry food.

However, as mentioned above, because chicken is low in iron and other essential minerals, a daily supplement of minerals and vitamins is required. It is also important, of course, to add adequate calcium to her diet. Both chicken and boiled rice contain low levels of calcium and therefore at least 2 tsp of DCP (dicalcium phosphate) should be added each day to the diet. Alternatively, a supplement such as Calci-D can be added to provide other vitamins and minerals. Should the bitch develop any further bouts of colitis, then obviously you should revert to the more bland chicken and rice diet.

30. Q I am writing to ask about my greyhound bitch, who is six months old. I have had her from ten weeks old. The trouble is her motions; they are always runny and yellow-green or brown in colour – some days she is not too bad. I have also got her litter brother, but I have no trouble with him.

We have been to a vet, who gave us pills and put her on a diet of fish and chicken, but this did not do any good. She is now back on normal foods. The list of foods is as follows: morning: 2 egg yolks, 3 wholemeal rusks, 1 Weetabix and milk, and later on in the morning a raw carrot; main meal: mincemeat of sheep's head or fish hearts or cheek, wholemeal bread with each of the above; also added is Mulipa vitamins, mixed vegetables, baby food in powder form and a little Beamax; also 3 times a week 1 cod-liver oil pill; not too much liver on vet's advice.

Both my dog and bitch have the same, but only the bitch has trouble. She is very fit and well in herself, apart from the runny motions.

A From your description, it seems that your bitch may be sensitive to something in her diet. In my opinion, it is more likely to be the raw carrot or the mincemeat of sheep's head or fish hearts that is upsetting her digestive system. Some greyhounds develop a digestive allergy to red meat and develop chronic diarrhoea.

I would suggest that you withdraw one of the possible causes out of her diet for at least a week on a rotational basis. In this way you may be able to identify what is causing her loose motions. It is also important to worm your bitch out on a regular basis.

In some greyhounds excessive amounts of mixed vegetables can cause a green diarrhoea, particularly if it is fed in a soft or very mushy form. I trust you are giving at least 2 slices of wholemeal bread with her main meal in the evening to ensure that she has adequate fibre and roughage for digestion.

I do not think there is much to worry about if she is fit and well in herself. However, should the problem become more persistent, then I would suggest you have the bitch thoroughly examined by your vet, just in case she has some internal disorder, or a heavy worm burden. A course of an antibiotic, such as aureomycin, from your vet, is often useful in settling the 'green' diarrhoea seen in some greyhounds. Consult you vet for advice.

RACING GREYHOUNDS

Q Could you enlighten me on the diet for racing greyhounds. I have read a few books, but am still at a loss. In all the diets I have read, they give examples for a dog that weighs 30kg. What if the dog weighs considerably more or less than that? **31.**

A Generally, most diets are compounded for the average 30kg or 60-65 lb greyhound. However, the individual needs of greyhounds vary considerably, and the diet may need to be adjusted for not only the weight of the greyhound, but also according to its appetite, likes and dislikes, and its rate of metabolism.

Generally, nervy greyhounds expend more energy from excitement and barking than the quieter types. Extra food, normally dry food, needs to be given in the colder months of the year to provide extra energy for warmth. Using lean beef as standard, on a 70 per cent meat based diet, a greyhound requires about 25g per kg bodyweight for racing. Therefore, a 25kg greyhound would require approximately 625g of lean beef and a 35kg dog would require approximately 875g. However, this amount may need to be adjusted, particularly in the heavier dog depending on the work-load, the intensity of training, and the dog's general condition.

Nowadays, with the high price of meat, most trainers are feeding a 20-30 per cent meat diet (200g) and 70-80 per cent dry food mix (450-500g) daily. Some trainers feed 100 per cent dry food, using feeding guidelines as on bag.

In early training, depending on the individual dog's bodyweight and the need to put on weight, the amounts may need to be increased by 5g per kg initially, and then reduced to the standard level once the dog reaches the required racing bodyweight and condition. Ideally, a greyhound in racing condition should have covering over the pinbones and ribs, which can be felt, and a firm belly when standing.

Raw meat is considered a natural food for dogs. It is better utilised when it is finely cut up, or, preferably, minced. Cooking does not improve digestibility of meat, but it can make it more tender. However, over-cooking can reduce overall digestibility of protein in dogs. Cooking also inactivates many vitamins, particularly vitamin C, vitamin B1, B6, B12 and folic acid, vitamins A and E. But it can kill unwanted germs in meat that could upset digestion. Generally, beef, mutton, chicken and horsemeat should not be cooked, but fed raw to greyhounds.

Dry food adds carbohydrates to the diet, and it does vary tremendously in the amount of protein because some are designed as complete foods and others as supplementary type foods. However, when added to meat, dry food is fed at the rate of approximately 5g per kg bodyweight, again depending on the dog's appetite and the stage of training. Generally, higher amounts are used in earlier training, and reduced by 10 per cent once the dog is racing regularly, in order to reduce the bulk of the ration.

This illustrates a greyhound in optimum condition for racing. As a guide, a greyhound in racing condition should be well and firmly muscled, covered over the pin bones and ribs with the last 2-3 ribs visible, and the belly firm and taut, without being tucked up. A good indication is the showing of "condition lines" along the rib cage and flank, as indicated above, with a ridge or muscle tuck in the lower flank border. The loss of hair from the thighs (bald thighs) in this particular greyhound, is due to hair shafts being cut off on a hessian (burlap) bag bedding cover.

Using wet weight of cooked vegetables, usually 5-7g per kg bodyweight, is quite adequate. Dry food can be easily changed to brown bread. Generally 2-3 slices of toasted wholemeal bread is an alternative to normal amounts of dry food added to a meat-based diet. When a dog is rested, usually the meat portion can be cut back to about 15g per kg and the dry food increased to 10g per kg.

Vitamins and minerals are important additives to the diet of greyhounds subjected to the stress of racing. Calcium, in particular, is deficient in most diets and should be added to the ration each day. However, once the greyhound is rested, there is less need for a continual intake of vitamins. Although the amount of calcium should be adequate to balance the diet, there is no need to add extra to meet the increased turnover during racing.

32. Q **Could you please give me a short list – say a daily list – of the vitamins you should feed, and how much you should give to a racing greyhound? There are so many vitamins that owners get confused. I have heard some trainers say sometimes a certain vitamin would cancel out another. Can you give a dog too much of certain vitamins so that they would have the reverse effect?**

The daily diet I feed is: morning – 1 egg, 1/2 pint milk and cereal; 4 p.m – 1lb lean meat, 1lb brown bread, cabbage, carrots, onions and gravy. I keep water in the kennels at all times and also give my greyhound a marrow bone once or twice a week.

A A racing dog requires a balanced intake of vitamins each day in the diet. Certain vitamins, particularly vitamins A and E, must be taken in with food as they are not synthesised within the dog's body. Vitamin D can be synthesised in the skin, but it takes 2-3 hours of sunlight per day to provide sufficient in the normal diets fed to a racing greyhound.

Greyhounds that are kennelled for most of the day benefit from a supplement of vitamin D. This is because, if the diet is imbalanced in calcium and phosphorus, as can commonly occur in high meat diets, then extra amounts of vitamin D are required to avoid bone problems. Vitamin E is particularly important, as meat contains low levels of vitamin E and it deteriorates quite rapidly during storage, particularly when meat is frozen.

The B complex group of vitamins, vitamin C and vitamin K are synthesised within the dog's body during digestion. Extra amounts are obtained from the food, and supplements, particularly B complex and vitamin C, may be beneficial in dogs under stress.

In most cases it is best to add a balanced vitamin supplement recommended for greyhounds. It is difficult to add each individual vitamin from separate vitamin tablets or other sources. In most cases trainers add supplements, such as Feramo-Greyhound, which contains a balanced level sufficient to meet requirements of a racing greyhound.

The diet that you are giving seems quite adequate for a racing dog in work. However, the amount of bread seems a little excessive, but if your dog is not becoming too fat, then it does provide adequate carbohydrates for racing. If you are happy with your dog's performance, then stick to your present diet. However, to ensure the dog receives adequate vitamins, I would suggest that you add a proprietary supplement, formulated especially for greyhounds, to his evening meals.

Vitamin E and vitamin C, if fed, should be added to a separate meal, usually the morning meal, to avoid inter-reaction between vitamin E and C with iron and other minerals. Calcium is also very important in the diet of racing greyhounds. I would suggest that you add 3 tsp of dicalcium phosphate to the evening meal to balance up the high amount of phosphorus you are adding with lean meat and brown bread. Alternatively, a proprietary supplement such as Calci-D can be provided daily at the recommended dose, based on the amount of meat you are feeding. The marrow bone, once a week, will provide some calcium, and also help to keep the dog's teeth clean and in good order.

33. Q Could you please advise me on the best food to give a greyhound as a pre-race feed. I know that a very light meal is given by most trainers on the day of the race at about lunchtime. Usually that consists mainly of meat gravy with, perhaps, a small handful of rusk and meat. Some trainers also put in glucose or honey. As I understand it, the glucose would have been broken down within the next hour and would be well out of the system by the time the dog raced, maybe 7 or 8 hours later.

I also wonder if we are leaving the dog for too long without a substantial meal, or should he race on a stomach that has been empty for several hours? In most kennels, the last substantial meal – not counting breakfasts and the pre-race feed are given over 30 hours prior to a race. Would the blood sugar levels be badly affected?

TRAINER'S TIP

When mixing a vitamin/mineral supplement into the meal, introduce by increasing the dose to the recommended amount over a 4-7 day period, particularly in greyhounds that are slow or fussy eaters. A general vitamin/mineral supplement, such as Feramo-Greyhound (example illustrated) is recommended to correct deficiencies or imbalances in meat based diets.

A Certainly, greyhounds are often given a lighter meal the night before a race, and depending on the time of racing, another meal as breakfast about 6-8 hours prior to the actual race time. However, there is no hard and fast rule about the time of feeding. The pre-race meal usually consists of the type of feed that you mentioned, such as meat gravy, rusk or dry food with about 200g or one-third lb lightly grilled meat. It seems to be an adequate meal to ensure that the greyhound maintains its energy levels and 'comfort' up until the time of the race.

Obviously, running a greyhound with an empty stomach may have a slight weight advantage over long distance races. When racing, greyhounds primarily use stored high energy substances and glycogen stored in their muscles, and blood glucose itself may not play an important part in replenishment during the actual race. However, if blood glucose is decreased prior to a race, the greyhound may be somewhat lethargic.

To my knowledge, there have been no studies carried out to determine the best time to feed greyhounds before racing. However, traditionally, most trainers give the greyhound a meal about 6-8 hours before a race, and over the years this seems to be satisfactory.

Adding glucose to a meal within 4-6 hours of a race is considered to be of no advantage to

TRAINER'S TIP

Supplementary Vitamin E (eg. White-E example illustrated) is widely used to help improve stamina and staying power in racing greyhounds. Vitamin E is considered by many authorities as the most beneficial of all vitamins routinely added to greyhound diets. Supplements of Vitamin E to overcome low or inadequate dietary levels are also beneficial in improving litter size, and vitality in brood bitches, fertility in older bitches, and sperm count in older stud dogs.

racing greyhounds. This is because glucose is rapidly absorbed and elevates blood sugar, and can switch on 'insulin' hormones that can then lower blood sugar. This could cause a dog to go into a depressed state within 4 hours of the feed. In some countries, substances containing long chain sugars are available to feed greyhounds and racing horses prior to racing. These are metabolised slower than glucose, and are considered by many to be helpful in greyhounds in particular, in ensuring that they maintain blood sugar levels for racing.

34. Q **I wonder if you could advise me on proper feeding and general caring for my dog who is three years, nine months. I have owned and trained many dogs, and I have had them reasonably fit and running pretty well. I have followed diets on feeding and and caring for this particular dog, but try as I might, I cannot get him to perform as he did nine months ago when he was going very fair times at most independents where I race.**

He is wormed regularly and well-exercised and well-fed. I have tried various tonics such as Metatone, Yeast Vite, etc., but to no avail. I realise I cannot expect much improvement as he is getting on a bit, although I still think there is plenty of running in him yet and he is free of any injury.

I am most concerned about his coat. My father always told me that if your dog is healthy inwardly, this should show on his coat. I have not been able to get his coat shining, even though he is combed and groomed every morning with a hard brush and hacksaw blade, and is generally well cared for. Could you suggest any method to bring his coat up and increase his general health.

A It is not uncommon for greyhounds over three years of age to drop in their performance, particularly when raced regularly. In many cases they perform quite well if their races are spaced two or three weeks apart. From your description, you have tried various supplements that sometimes are beneficial to racing greyhounds. However, considering his age, I would suggest that you try a supplement such as Fortex which contains a small amount of caffeine. Fortex is used as a tonic and can be useful as a 'pick-me-up' for a few days following racing, to allow a dog to recover more quickly. Obviously, it must be withdrawn prior to racing where products containing caffeine are not allowed under the rules. When using a product such as Fortex give 8ml once a day for 3 days or so, reducing to 6ml daily for a couple of days, then 4ml daily in the morning feeds. To help coat condition, a supplement containing vitamin A, iron and trace minerals such as Feramo-Greyhound would be beneficial.

35. Q **I wondered if you would help me out with my whippet's diet. What vitamins should I give to get the best performance? My bitch's racing weight is 27 lb (12.3 kg).**

A Racing whippets normally require similar diet to the racing greyhound, but obviously in proportion to their bodyweight. As a guideline give about 50-60 per cent of the amount given to a greyhound. There are various types of diets suitable for whippets from 70 per cent raw meat to a 50/50 balance of meat and dry foods.

I suggest that you use the following as a guideline:

BREAKFAST: 1/4-1/3 cup milk, 1/2 cup dry food or 1 slice wholemeal bread, 1/2 tbsp honey, 50-100iu White-E, calcium powder (e.g. 1/2 tsp Dicalcium Phosphate – DCP), one raw egg yolk, twice a week.

EVENING MEAL: Raw meat – 200-250g lean beef or 300g lean chicken mince, 1/2-3/4 cup dry food. Alternatively, a low meat diet could contain 100g mince and 2 cupfuls of a 20 per cent protein dry food. A total dry food diet may also be suitable, with added minerals and vitamins. Vegetables – 1/2 cup (cooked), water (mixed into meal) – 1/2-3/4 cup, calcium powder (3/4 tsp DCP), vitamins (e.g. 1/2 tsp Feramo-Greyhound). During hot weather, 1/2tsp of Betacel in the meal is recommended. The whippet should get enough salt from the dry food.

You may need to adjust these guidelines depending on the availability of the meat. In cold weather add an extra 1/4 cup dry food to the evening meal as extra energy. Give about 50g liver or kidney twice weekly for variety if you wish (1oz/30g).

The above diet may have to be adjusted to the likes and dislikes of the whippet. Ideally, the whippet should be maintained in a condition with covering over the ribs so that they can still be felt, and a firm belly area when standing.

Chicken mince is a useful alternative to beef if available at a competitive price. However, being a white meat, it is naturally lower in the blood forming minerals, iron, copper and cobalt (Vitamin B12). Always supplement chicken based diets for racing greyhounds with a vitamin/mineral supplement containing these minerals. If such a supplement is not provided daily, greyhounds may lose form due to low-grade anaemia within 3-4 weeks.

36. Q Can you settle an argument for me with regard to feeding? Do racing greyhounds need the 27 per cent protein as found in most complete meals, e.g. Wafcol, Kasco? We have been told that such a high protein diet can damage a dog's kidneys etc. Is this so, and what are the first signs of kidney damage?

If a dog is being fed on meat mince with, say, an 18 per cent protein mixer, with a vitamin supplement (SA37), is this sufficient protein to get the best from the dog?

Our vet has told us that 22 per cent protein is enough for any dog – is this so in greyhounds? Our dogs race once a week over 482 yards.

A In most cases, racing greyhounds in work do not need an excessively high protein diet such as would normally be fed to a growing puppy. In fact, racing greyhounds perform and race well on a 20-23 per cent protein diet. This is usually made up of about 70 per cent meat mince and 30 per cent of a 16-18 per cent protein dry food, as you suggest.

Excessively high protein diets are not only expensive, but many trainers believe their dogs do not perform as well. Research studies indicate that, provided the energy content of the food meets the requirement for racing, protein requirements are not significantly greater than those required for a dog at rest. Therefore, a diet containing 70 per cent meat mince and 30 per cent dry food (18-20 per cent protein) is usually quite sufficient for racing greyhounds. In fact, a diet with 30 per cent meat or less and 70 per cent dry food is more economical. Dry foods have improved in quality and greyhounds can be raced on a total dry food diet.

Studies have shown that hard working dogs, such as racing sled dogs, do require extra protein in their diets. This protein will provide some energy for racing, and the rest for maintaining muscle strength and other body functions. There is no evidence that a 27 per cent protein diet would cause kidney damage. This is because dogs have adapted to a relatively high protein diet, and unless kidney damage was caused by some other problem, they can normally metabolise a relatively high protein diet. However, recent research suggests that a racing greyhound will benefit from a higher protein meal (24-27 per cent protein) fed for 2 meals after each hard race. Higher protein meals during recovery help to replace damaged muscle and blood protein after racing. The first signs of kidney damage vary according to the cause, but would normally show as reduced performance, poor appetite, and vomitting in severe cases.

It is also important to ensure your greyhound gets adequate exercise. This will stimulate his appetite and also promote muscle and body development. If possible, take the pup for a 1-1 1/2 km walk each day, or alternatively allow the pup to have 20 minutes of free running in a large yard or park. You can also go for a jog for 1 km with the pup on a lead. Excessive exercise will burn up too much energy and reduce the growth rate. However, ensure the pup does not become too big or heavy, otherwise excessive bodyweight may cause extra stress on his developing bone structure.

Although bread is useful as a filler in a diet, it only contains about 8 per cent protein and 3 per cent fat which may not be sufficient for a growing pup. Bread could be mixed into the mid-day stew as an alternative to biscuit, if you wish. Ideally, a 21-24 per cent protein biscuit should be used in the ration. Avoid the use of a large amount of liver as it can over-supply certain vitamins in the diet. Liver should be limited to 50g twice a week. If the pup will not eat the morning meal with milk, then flavour the milk with 1 tbsp honey, or a beef or chicken cooking cube.

37. Q I have had a bitch since she was eight weeks old and she is now 14 months old. She is a Saluki/greyhound lurcher. I have decided to get her into racing as there are a lot of lurcher shows which have racing after the show.

She stands 25 inches to the shoulder, and she weighs 42 lb at the moment. I want to know what food would be best for her and what quantities to give her, and what extra vitamins etc. it would be advisable to give her. What is the ideal weight for such a dog in order to get the best racing results. I have made lots of enquiries and I have had many conflicting items of advice.

A Basically, the same principles and dietary management apply to all types of racing dogs, including Saluki-cross breeds. In many cases, since a bitch such as yours would also be shown, it is even more important to ensure that the dog is on a balanced diet. In most cases, the racing weight would be 55-65 lb, particularly if the dog was also prepared for show purposes. The ideal weight largely depends on the build of the bitch, and you should aim at maintained bodyweight, so that the bitch has a thin covering of fat over her ribs and body. However, you could also check with other owners of similar bred dogs and take note of the condition that they keep their dogs in and get best results in lurcher races.

As a suggestion, the following dietary guidelines could be used as a ration for your racing Saluki:

MORNING MEAL: Milk – 100-150ml, dry food (17-21 per cent protein) – 75g (3/4 cup). Alternatively, 2 slices toasted wholemeal bread, eggs – 1 raw yolk or one cooked egg, or 50g of cheese if available.

EVENING MEAL: Raw meat – e.g. 200g lean to medium beef (mince the meat fresh each day), or alternatively, mix half lean beef and half chicken meat. If you wish to feed dry food – 400g (4 cups) for her present size; increase as she fills out and grows.

Fresh water should be available at all times. Change daily and keep the bowl clean. A general vitamin and mineral supplement such as Feramo-Greyhound should provide those nutrients to balance the diet and ensure health and vitality. A supplement of calcium powder such as DCP, given as 2-3 tsp daily, will provide essential needs for calcium to maintain bone strength.

If your bitch is racing regularly, particularly during hot weather or you travel a long distance to shows and races, then a supplement of physiological salts may also be necessary. A supplement such as Betacel, 1 tsp in the morning milk, would be quite sufficient for your type of bitch. This will ensure that she does not dehydrate when travelling and maintains good coat condition for showing. It will also help to ensure that she does not develop a body salt deficiency which could reduce her racing performance.

Q I am writing to ask you for advice about my greyhound bitch. She is just over two years old and weighs about 58 lb. We have just started to race her and she is running about once a week. The problem with her is that she will only eat green tripe, fresh from the slaughterhouse, preferably in a big piece that she can gnaw at. I am worried because I have been told that tripe is a poor quality food and that my bitch will not produce her best form on a diet of tripe. She will occasionally have milk at breakfast, but not much else. I am also worried that she might not be getting the necessary vitamins. Please tell me if there is sufficient protein in tripe and what I can do to improve her diet.** **38.**

A Unfortunately, tripe is low in energy, protein and fat. It has only about two-thirds of the energy content of beef, about 12 per cent protein, and 2 per cent fat. It is usually best fed cooked and best mixed on a 50/50 basis with other meat. You should also add extra fat to

The same principles of dietary management apply to all types of racing dogs, including coursing dogs.

the diet, such as 1 1/2-2 tbsp lard or dripping to boost the fat content to ensure the greyhound gets adequate fat for digestion, and also to prevent dehydration, particularly in the summer months.

Tripe is a poor quality food and you will probably not get the best out of your bitch unless you feed her other things, including other meats and dry foods. Generally, greyhounds require about 20 per cent average protein in the diet to provide sufficient for exercise and muscle development. Therefore it is imperative that you increase the protein content of her ration to meet the normal recommended standards. I would suggest you try to wean her off the predominantly tripe diet by providing one-third meat and two-thirds dry food (approximately 700g evening meal for her size), and grating fresh green tripe over the food to encourage her to eat it. Although it might take some time for her to become accustomed to the new food, it will certainly be nutritious for her and enable her to perform to ability. Sometimes the diet can be made more palatable by grating 2 tbsp of cheese over it and this may help her to accept the new diet as you slowly replace the tripe.

39.Q **I am writing to ask your advice about my three coursing dogs. I feed my dogs on 1/4 Purina Greyhound food, 1/4 Vitalin and 1/4 meat. What I would like to know is, could I introduce vitamin White-E to them and Orovite '7', which is a multi-vitamin, in the same feed? (I feed them once a day). I have heard that some vitamins and irons destroy White-E.**

A Generally, if your greyhounds are maintaining their body condition and are coursing successfully, then you are feeding them an adequate diet, although you did not give details of your complete diet.

As regards the use of a product such as White-E in combination with a multi-vitamin supplement such as Orovite '7', there is no problem in adding vitamin E to the same feed mix. This is because Orovite '7', a human preparation, containing only vitamins and no destructive minerals. Therefore, the combination of White-E and Orovite '7' could be added to the same single meal that you give to your greyhounds each day.

If you wish to supplement with iron in particular, which could be useful if your greyhounds are lacking stamina and are 'pale' around the gums, then a liquid iron tonic, such as Ironcyclen, could be given by syringe over the back of the tongue a few minutes prior to feeding each day. Obviously, you should also ensure that your greyhounds are regularly wormed, so as to remove blood-sucking worms which would also make them anaemic.

Q **I have a two-year-old dog which I run over 475 metres and 280 metres every other** **40.** **week, on Fridays. My problems are feeding. His morning feed, after a run in the park, is 8oz Pasco's 18 per cent protein dry feed, 1 cup of Cornflakes, 4 tablets of Vetzyme B Plus E, 2 tbsp sunflower oil, mixed with milk. His evening meal, after a run in the park, is 4oz brown bread, 8oz Pasco's, 1 tbsp Glucose C, and 1/2 cup mixed, chopped vegetables (watered down). I feed the above from Saturday evening to Monday evening. From Tuesday morning I feed a 24 per cent protein instead of the Pasco's 18 per cent in the morning and evening meal.**

My dog is very fast off the boxes and stays the 475 metres well, but he is panting very heavily for 15 minutes or more after his racing, with the occasional cough. He was wormed a month ago and the vet has passed him fit.

He has a run in the park every morning and night, from Saturday until Wednesday night. On Thursdays I walk him for 1 mile morning and night. On Friday morning I just take him out to empty himself. On race days I feed him 6 shortcake biscuits, white of egg, 4 Vetzyme B Plus E tablets, 1 tbsp Glucose C with milk at 12 noon (as he races at 8-8.30 p.m.). Am I doing justice to the dog?

A I have examined the level of energy in the feed that you are currently feeding your greyhound. It appears adequate to provide sufficient energy to meet the dog's exercise level. Providing the greyhound is maintaining his weight, then he is getting adequate levels of energy to match his requirements.

From your letter, you state that you race on Fridays. You also mentioned that you increase the protein level in the diet from 18 per cent to 24 per cent from Tuesday to Thursday. In most cases, it is recommended to increase the protein after a race to assist recovery after racing.

On race-day, you state that you are feeding shortcake biscuits, egg white and your normal vitamin tablets. It appears that you may not be giving sufficient energy actually on race day to meet his needs. I would suggest that you give a morning breakfast as normal, then follow-up with the special lighter feed at noon. Generally, it would be much better to give him egg yolk rather than white of egg, as an egg yolk contains five times as much energy as the white.

You are basing your diet on dry food completely. Generally, dry foods do not contain as much iron and other 'blood building' nutrients as meat-based diets. Although your dog stays well over the race distance, he pulls up panting, suggesting perhaps anaemia or a lung condition. Obviously, a blood count taken by your vet would be useful to determine whether anaemia was the underlying cause. The occasional cough after racing could be due to built-up phlegm in the back of the throat.

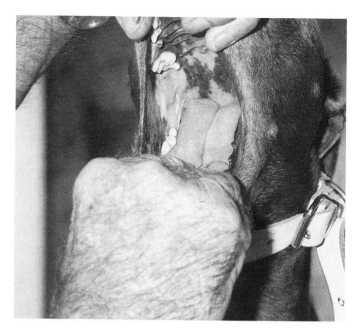

Pale gums and tongue signifies anaemia or a poor blood count due to heavy worm burdens, or a diet deficient in blood building minerals, such as iron and copper – a common problem on chicken meat diets which are low in these minerals. Worm out the animal, and give a daily supplement of iron and vitamins, such as Feramo-Greyhound.

Again, a check by your vet would be able to determine whether this is hampering his performance.

Electrolyte imbalances may also cause distress after racing. From your diets, you are feeding no specialised electrolyte supplement on a regular basis. I suggest that you start feeding electrolyte supplements containing potassium (e.g. Betacel) particularly during the warm summer months. It may also be useful to put the greyhound on to a general vitamin/mineral supplement containing iron (e.g. Feramo-Greyhound) or other supplements containing iron and trace minerals. These supplements would be indicated if the greyhound shows anaemia.

I trust that you are regularly worming your dog. If you are racing him regularly once a week, then he should stay fit enough for racing. However, if you are racing every fortnight, then I feel the dog should be trialled, or at least galloped over 300 metres once a week between races, in order to keep him as fit as possible.

41. Q **Could you please explain a little about a greyhound's digestive system. As I understand it, their systems are very weak and can suffer if fed too much protein.**

I have heard of greyhounds being fed tinned dog food and their stomachs just do not seem able to cope. Is this a reason why trainers 'let their dogs down' and give them lower protein foods before a major racing season?

A There is no real scientific evidence to suggest that greyhounds have a 'weaker' digestive system than other dogs. However, greyhounds do tend to be more sensitive to changes in the amount and types of food than most other breeds of dogs.

Greyhounds require a high energy diet; this is why they fail to do well when fed tinned dog food. Tinned dog food contains low levels of energy, fat and protein, and really needs to be supplemented with dry food, bread or table scraps to give it an energy level above maintenance. In many cases, a greyhound's condition will fall away if it is maintained on a tinned food diet.

Generally, a greyhound must have an adequate level of protein in its diet to help maintain its muscle mass and provide nutrients for building blood, bone and muscle. The diet should contain up to 30-35 per cent of high-quality protein, and most meat-based diets, with extra contributed from high-quality dry foods, will provide this level of protein. Where adequate energy is provided for work and exercise by meat and dry food based diets, the energy level required to allow the dog to perform will provide adequate protein.

Training also decreases the use of protein as an energy source during muscular exercise. However, the type of protein given to the greyhound affects its digestibility. Meat-based proteins are better digested than vegetable proteins. One of the factors that reduces protein digestibility is over-cooking meat protein.

There is certainly no evidence to support the use of extra high protein diets to enhance physical exercise in racing greyhounds. Studies have shown that there is no relationship between digestible protein intake and performance in greyhounds. However, in practice, when muscle mass and the blood is being developed early in training, there is some logic in increasing the protein content of the ration at this time. Where excess protein is given to a greyhound, it may actually affect its performance. Elimination of excess protein uses valuable energy sources. The elevated waste passed in urine, coupled with the increased body temperature from 'burning' protein, may reduce the overall performance of the greyhound.

Many trainers therefore feed extra fat and carbohydrates to provide energy for greyhounds in training, whilst maintaining them on an adequate level of protein, provided simply in meat and dry food. There is no benefit in adding sources of high protein meal such as soya bean, etc., to the greyhound's ration. In many cases these too can cause digestive upsets.

However, after racing there seems to be benefit in giving greyhounds a higher protein diet for 2-3 meals after each race. This will help to provide extra protein to overcome muscle damage and rebuild muscle tissue after racing. Therefore, many trainers increase the protein content of the diet by adding a high protein dry food for 1 or 2 meals after each race. This seems to help greyhounds maintain their muscle mass on a more even basis, and they perform more consistently, particularly when racing on a regular weekly basis.

In summary, a higher protein diet is fed early in training to help build muscle and blood, which is then decreased as the greyhound becomes fit and requires extra energy for fast work for trialling. After racing and a hard trial, higher protein meals are useful in helping to provide the raw materials for re-building damaged muscles.

Q **I have been reading a book on diet recently, which made great store of not mixing certain food types or vitamins in the same meal. In your opinion, should protein be fed at a different time from carbohydrate? Which vitamins should not be fed together? Finally, could you please give me your opinion on feeding milk.** **42.**

A Certainly, it is unwise to mix vitamin E and vitamin C in the same foods as iron and copper tonics that are given to greyhounds as a blood building tonic. Therefore it is important to add vitamin E and vitamin C, if these are being supplemented, to the morning meal along with electrolytes. Add the iron and other mineral tonics to the evening meal. This will avoid any interaction between the vitamins and minerals, and ensure that your greyhounds obtain the maximum benefit from the supplementary vitamins.

Other vitamins, such as B complex vitamins, are also prone to deterioration when mixed with iron supplements, and therefore it is recommended that concentrated forms of these vitamins, such as contained in Rebound tablets etc. should be given directly over the tongue prior to feeding the greyhound with foods supplemented with iron and other minerals. As regards feeding protein and carbohydrate, there have been some recent practical observations that suggest some benefit from segregating these two feed components into different meals. Generally, carbohydrates fed in the morning feed as cereal-based biscuits, rice or even pasta, and protein meals with meat given in the evening, seem to improve the health and performance of greyhounds.

One trainer reported that his dogs appeared to digest their food better, and seemed to perform better after 1-2 weeks of this segregation of carbohydrates and proteins. However, there needs to be more work carried out on a practical basis to see whether this segregation of feeds is beneficial in the longer term. Theoretically, according to some of the literature published for humans, this type of feeding tends to give better digestion overall, and therefore may generally improve health.

As regards feeding milk, again this is a subject of much debate over recent times. One of the theories is that milk is really a feed for young animals, and it is not very well digested in adult greyhounds. This is because the milk sugar in milk, once the greyhound is weaned for more than 1-2 months, cannot be broken down efficiently and acts as an intestinal irritant rather than being beneficial in the long term.

However, there is another school of thought that considers that if milk is given on a regular basis from puppyhood up until racing, then greyhounds continue to benefit as they retain the ability to

TRAINER'S TIP

Older breeding and retired greyhounds benefit from a yeast and B-vitamin supplement to improve appetite and general vitality. Daily administration of two Rebound tablets (example illustrated) is also recommended as a vitamin booster for the two days before and after each race, particularly if a greyhound is to race again within 5-7 days.

digest milk sugars even in adulthood. Certainly, if a greyhound is weaned off milk at an early age, then, theoretically, milk would provide only small amounts of calcium and some protein to the adult greyhound. However, as many greyhounds like to drink milk, it can help to overcome dehydration problems in greyhounds that are prone to dehydration due to excitement, hard walking, or the warmer weather.

Many trainers claim that milk 'softens' a greyhound, but this has not been proven on a scientific basis. Recently, the use of whole fresh dairy cream, mixed at the rate of 250ml or 1 cup of cream into 1 litre of water to make a creamy fat emulsion, appears to have some merits, in that a greyhound would be able to digest this feed and use the fat for energy. However, the amount of this type of cream emulsion would have to be restricted, depending on the work-load, otherwise the greyhound would put on excessive bodyweight which would in turn hamper its performance.

Q I wonder if you can help me with a couple of points regarding the long-term effects of different types of feeding on a greyhound's digestive system? I am told that it was once a standard practice to change a dog's feeding in tandem with its fitness, and that once a dog had peaked it would frequently be given 'rester's feed' in its diet to ease a burden on its digestive system. I understand that the rester's feed basically consisted of bread and **43.**

TRAINER'S TIP

Many trainers query if meat should be fed in "chunks", or coarsely minced. As a guideline, cubes or chunks of meat up to 2.5cm (1") in size are adequately digested by racing greyhounds. However, very finely minced meat is not retained for an adequate time in the stomach and small bowel, and nutritional benefit of the meat may be reduced. Meat should be warmed to room temperature before feeding as meat from a refrigerator may cause stomach discomfort and risk of vomiting after eating.

vegetables, with no meat to cut down on the protein content. After a short rest the greyhound would be put back into training and the protein content increased. Does this make commonsense or is it an unscientific method that would not stand up to modern knowledge of feeding and the effects on the body?

Secondly, do you agree with the process of vomiting a greyhound to clear its system? This is still regular practice in some kennels, but, again, it seems to be an old-fashioned idea that has survived the years.

A Certainly, there has been a common practice over the years to 'freshen-up' a greyhound after two or three hard races by giving three or days days of watery stews that are easily digested. It certainly appears to correct dehydration problems in greyhounds during the warmer weather, and many greyhounds race on quite successfully.

During hot weather I have found that it is helpful to try to give a hard-raced greyhound about seven to ten days of meaty stews with moistened dry food, and free run into a larger yard, particularly if a greyhound is showing signs of 'training-off', or stress from the rigours of racing.

TRAINER'S TIP

The addition of a couple of eggs to the first meal after a hard race increases the protein content and may assist in muscle protein rebuilding. A simple way to improve the acceptance and digestion of an egg without damaging its protein and nutritional content by cooking, is to crack the egg into a cup. Fill the cup with boiling water. Allow to stand for 30-60 seconds until the egg whites develop, drain off the excess water, and add the egg(s) to the meal.

As you mentioned, bread and vegetables are often used, but I have found that a stew-type consistency is probably better accepted by greyhounds.

After racing it is a good idea to increase the protein content for one or two meals by giving two egg yolks or two cups of high protein dry food. This increases the protein content to help muscle repair in the post-race period. Although decreasing the protein content during the rest period is a consequence of feeding bread and vegetable type diets, it probably has no beneficial effect on easing the dog's digestive burden. However, the increased moisture content in the diet, and general laxative properties of the meal, certainly help to stimulate the greyhound's general well-being, appetite and recovery after hard racing.

As regards vomiting a greyhound to clear his system, this practice is still thought to be beneficial to greyhounds. Certainly, many greyhounds appear to 'freshen-up' after being stimulated to vomit, but generally it is now considered to be unnecessary and stressful to the greyhound. Nowadays, many trainers are giving a regular dose of a laxative to gently clean out any waste products in the bowels, and soften the stools.

This can be given two or three days prior to racing, and in many cases greyhounds appear to tolerate this well, without the need to vomit bile. However, there are still trainers who believe that vomit biling is a necessary pastime; obviously their opinion will not change with modern developments. However, in my opinion, laxative biling once every seven to ten days does have benefit in helping a greyhound to cope with a concentrated diet, and as many trainers report, helps to relieve build-up of a 'biley throat' or froth in the back of the throat area.

Q **I would like your opinion on whether to give extra vitamins to dogs fed on high** **44.** **protein expandable food. I have recently changed over from meat and vegetables etc., and when feeding that way I used to give White-E ascorbic acid in the morning and Feramo D at night. I have two bitches aged 3 years and 16 months racing regularly and a 5 month old pup.**

A Generally, the supplements that you are feeding at present would be adequate to meet the needs for vitamins and the majority of minerals. However, in some cases, greyhounds in hard work and racing regularly respond to additional B complex vitamins and vitamin E. Vitamin E, as in White-E, is often destroyed in dry foods and frozen meat during storage, and a supplement of 100-200iu helps increase performance and stamina. However, I suggest that you check the level of calcium contained in the dry feed, as you may need to add extra calcium to the night feed. A racing greyhound bitch would require up to 7g of calcium per day. Calculate the amount of calcium contained in the weight of dry food provided from the percentage (grams per 100g or approximately 1 cupful) given to the greyhound. In some cases this will fall short of the required 7g per day. Milk contains 300mg calcium per cupful. Add the total amount together, and add a supplement such as Calci-D to make up the shortfall. In a good quality dry food containing 1-1.5 per cent calcium, additional calcium is not normally required.

WEIGHT / CONDITION LOSS

Q **I am a permit trainer and have a few dogs which I race around the East of England. I** **45.** **have been racing for about three years now. I recently bought a bitch from London. She should weigh 26.2 kg. I have had her for six weeks now, and she has lost weight rapidly. I put her on more rusk but she is still not putting weight on as fast as I would like. I**

know she was on injections that stopped her season and I wonder whether taking her off those was the reason for her weight-loss.

She now weighs 25.2 and that is a great improvement on a couple of weeks ago. I have wormed her; she is kept warm and she certainly appears to be well in herself. I feed her on 1/2 pint milk and 2 1/2 oz Weetabix, glucose and egg (raw) and White-E, and in the evening 1lb mince, 6oz racing rusk, 5oz cabbage (raw), B12, yeast, cod-liver oil, vitamin C and seaweed powder. I don't think she was fed as much meat before I had her. Is there anything to worry about? I give all my dogs all these vitamins every night. Am I in danger of over-supplementing?

There is one other thing I have noticed. After racing, my new bitch does not drink water at all. This seems strange as her mouth must be full of sand. My brother, who is also a permit trainer, gives his dogs a pint of baby's milk as soon as they come off and, of course, they drink it. I know mine would drink it too, but is this wise?

After racing I like to clean my dogs out because I know they must swallow a lot of sand and muck. I use Epsom Salts or Milk of Magnesia for this. I don't like doing this a lot, as it must weaken the dogs – is there anything I can use other than this?

I know I have raised many points, but vets in this area are not greyhound specialists and never seem to have time to answer my questions.

A It is not uncommon for bitches that have been given injections to prevent them coming on season to lose weight when the hormone therapy is withdrawn. However, this effect is normally overcome within one or two months, and the bitch should stabilize her weight and start to improve. I would suggest that this could be the underlying reason for the weight-loss when you first bought your bitch. You have certainly done everything possible to help increase her nutritional efficiency. The diet you are feeding is certainly adequate, and she should stabilize and increase her weight on this type of diet. Normally, I find that excessive amounts of raw cabbage can sometimes cause digestive problems, and can reduce the benefit of a good well-balanced diet. Therefore, I would suggest that you cut the amount of cabbage in half to avoid such a problem.

There should be no problems in feeding the amounts of vitamins that you are currently giving your bitch. Greyhounds under stress certainly require extra vitamins, and they simply extract what they need and pass the rest out in their stools or water. The daily supplement of White-E, in particular, would be beneficial to increase her muscle strength and stamina.

I would avoid feeding more than two raw eggs per day, as they can cause an imbalance of certain vitamins, and do not feed too much vitamin C as this can imbalance the diet and lead to performance problems. About 250mg of vitamin C per day is usually adequate for a racing greyhound. Double this amount can be given on the morning after a race to help the dog recover, along with extra B complex.

It is important to wash out your bitch's mouth once she comes off the track to clean away saliva, foam and sand particles. Also wash the feet to cool them down and remove sand. There should be no worries in giving your bitch a drink of milk following a race. I find that 1-1 1/2 cups is usually sufficient, as excessive milk may cause a digestive upset and scouring. It may also be a good idea to give 1 tsp of an electrolyte mix such as Betacel in the milk each morning, and also 1/2 tsp in the milk after a race. Many trainers like to clean their dogs out after a race. However, this can sometimes lead to dehydration and cause a digestive upset which may hamper recovery. A dose of 2 tsp of Agaro C in the feed would help to clear her bowels after racing. Administration of 4-6ml of Neutrade over the tongue would help flush her kidneys after racing.

Q I recently purchased a greyhound fawn dog. He is approximately three years old. He **46.** is well out of condition coat-wise, and in general overall health. It is roughly five years since I owned and trained my own dogs. and I would like advice on vitamins and such that would help to bring him on, also to give him a nice coat, as he is very dry at the moment.

A Obviously, it is most important to thoroughly worm out your greyhound, and perhaps repeat the worming again in 4 weeks after the initial worming. Seek advice from your veterinary surgeon on the best type of wormer to use for this purpose.

The addition of 2 tsp polyunsaturated cooking oil each day will help to improve coat condition, particularly when it is given with a vitamin/mineral supplement containing trace elements such as zinc, copper and iron. A supplement such as Feramo-Greyhound would contain these trace elements, plus other essential vitamins which will help the general health and coat condition.

Q I would be grateful if you could advise me as to putting weight on my greyhounds. **47.** One is a small bitch approximately 25 1/2 inches tall. weighing 42lbs. We have had for about six weeks. During this time she has been fully inoculated and wormed. At present she is being fed two meals per day: 3 Weetabix and 1/2 pint milk for breakfast at 7.30 a.m., and 1lb Beta racer (soaked) with 1 pint water for the main meal at 4 p.m.

My other greyhound is a large, rather unsettled bitch, just purchased from the Irish sales. We were told she had travelled badly coming over on the ferry, and was therefore out of condition and underweight. We were told that she should weigh at least 65 lbs. At present she weighs 58 lb, and she stands approximately 28 inches high. She was given the minimum of vaccinations just before bringing her to England and we have since had these, plus parvo, completed.

This bitch has 4 Weetabix and 1/2 pint milk for breakfast at 7.30 a.m., and 1lb 3oz Beta racer (soaked) for her main meal at 4 p.m. She seems unable to manage any more than this and needs constant encouragement to finish her food. She had a large amount of hard, encrusted tartar on her teeth which has now been removed, revealing healthy teeth.

Regularly check the teeth for tartar build-up to reduce the risk of bad breath and tonsillitis in racing greyhounds. Regular teeth care in young animals ensure retired breeding greyhounds have fewer dental problems.

Both bitches are about 18 months old and have come from kennels. They now live in the house, sharing a large foam bed, covered with carpet, and raised off the ground. They receive at least 1½ hours walking a day, and an occasional run when it is safe to do so.

The milk given for breakfast is a powdered milk-mix, served weaker than suggested, as fresh milk seems to have made their motions loose as do the 'memo' biscuits we were advised to give them in between meals by a trainer. Their condition has improved since coming to us, but we seem unable to put sufficient weight on them.

In the short time we have had her, the small bitch has been treated by our vet for high temperature, and when she recovered from this bodily infection she had to be treated for an eye infection which has not yet fully cleared up.

A It is not uncommon for unsettled nervy bitches to fail to put on adequate weight. In many cases, nervous behaviour makes a 'delicate' eater, and the dog difficulty in consuming its full feed. After looking at your diets, it appears that they may not meet the demand for energy that is used up with 1½ hours walking per day. In nervy, unsettled greyhounds, a combination of excitement and walking for long distances utilises far more energy than they would be able to obtain on a diet such as you are feeding. As you mention, it is a good idea not to feed too much fresh milk as it may cause loose motions. In the winter-time greyhounds kept in cold kennels will also lose extra energy keeping themselves warm. However, your dogs are well cared for and kept warm. I would suggest you add about 1 cup of the Beta racer to the morning Weetabix for both bitches. This will increase the amount of energy added to the morning meals. As they are only young bitches, I would also suggest that they be put on to vitamin E, such as White-E, to ensure that adequate of this important vitamin is available for muscle development and strength to prepare them for racing.

Although there may be some reason why you are feeding dried type foods, I would suggest that these types of bitches may do better on the addition of some raw meat to their diet. If you wish to feed a predominantly dry food diet, then I would suggest that you add about 1/2lb minced beef or a mixture of beef and chicken to boost the protein and energy levels in their diet. To help them put on weight more quickly it would be useful to include about 1½ tbsp of lard in their diet to provide extra energy as fat.

I would also suggest that you cut their walking back to about 30-40 minutes a day until they start to gain weight. Excessive walking can tire greyhounds, reduce appetite, and prevent them from putting on adequate weight gain. However, I assume that you are conditioning your greyhounds by walking and occasional sprints over the first six weeks of their training programme. Once they start to put on weight, then you can adjust their diets and exercise to maintain their weight.

In the evening meal it would be useful to add a mineral supplement such as Feramo, and extra calcium. A half pound of brisket bone given every second day will help provide some extra calcium to their diet. This will also help to naturally clean their teeth and prevent tartar build-up, as was a problem in the larger bitch.

48. Q I have six pups which are 13 months old. They have all had hand slips to inside and outside hares, and are all chasing very well, but I am worried about their weight. They are all very light. They are kennelled in twos – dog and bitch, dog and bitch, and two dogs. They have a big concreted paddock (20ft x 8ft) and seem to be on the go all day, running up and down. They have all been wormed regularly with Panacur.

Their diet consists of Beta racing meal with broth added for taste; milk and glucose with

brown bread for their breakfast. They are all very good eaters, but they are very slim. They have all just finished a heavy moult, getting their new coats in, and they look in very good health apart from the weight.

A It appears that your pups are highly active and are running off their weight and are therefore failing to develop as you would like. Although you did not mention the exact quantities of feed that you are giving, I would suggest that you consider placing a bowl of dry food in the corner of their run for them to snack between your large meals.

Alternatively, if you have time available, give them a midday meal as well as the morning and evening meals. I would think that providing extra dry food on an ad lib basis would be the most suitable, and I am sure that you would see a big difference in your pups.

It certainly doesn't hurt them to run around a lot, but sometimes when energy is lacking in the diet they fail to fill out and develop properly. Although you have been worming regularly with the one type of wormer, it might be advisable to take a sample of stools to your vet for a worm egg test. This way you would find whether your worming programme is adequate.

You may wish to check the protein levels in the diet as well, as growing pups fed on a basically dry food diet would need about 24-27 per cent protein in the dry food. Alternatively, you could add 50/50 meat for the evening meal to boost the protein levels. However, from your description, your dogs appear to be in good health and I am sure that an increase in energy by giving dry food on an ad lib basis during the day would ensure that they develop to their full potential.

FLUIDS

Q I have two dogs that I train and they seem to drink very little water. I always leave fresh water available but they never seem to drink it. Can you please tell me how I can recognise the symptoms of dehydration and how it affects the performance of the dog?

49

A The signs of chronic dehydration include dull, dry coat, reduced elasticity of the skin when it is pinched up, sunken eye, poor performance, and slow recovery from racing. Many dogs also pass small quantities of dark urine and do not drink very much water. Even though fresh water is available, such as you leave out for your dogs, chronically dehydrated dogs do not drink it. This is because both water and body salts are lost from the body, and the normal thirst response stimulus does not act to make them feel thirsty and want to drink water.

Probably the best clinical sign of dehydration is a dull, dry coat, sunken eye, and tendency to pass small amounts of dark, thick urine. In some cases, when the diet is adequate in fluid, particularly a stew-based diet, greyhounds will obtain most of their fluid requirements from this type of food. Therefore, they may appear not to drink very much fresh water.

If you suspect that your dogs are suffering from dehydration then I suggest you provide a daily supplement of electrolytes, and in severe cases, extra potassium salt such as 1 Slow-K tablet daily. Make sure the dry food is dampened to a moist, but not 'sloppy' consistency to provide more fluid to compensate for the poor drinking. Feeding a watery meat stew two or three times a week also helps to ensure additional water intake.

Q Please could you settle an argument for me. A friend of mine does not believe in keeping water with his dogs. I say a dog should never be without fresh, clean drinking water. He only believes in giving cabbage water to the dogs, and only before they go

50.

back into the kennel. Lat year, he had a dog that had kidney and bladder trouble, and I reckon it was through giving cabbage water all the time, and not providing clean water to flush out the dog's kidneys out, that was the cause of the problem.

He has had dogs for years and is very stubborn and old-fashioned in his ways. Recently, my dogs had a stomach bug with diarrhoea and he told me to take their water away. I refused, as, if a dog has diarrhoea and is losing body fluid, you should give plenty to drink to stop them becoming dehydrated. He replied that water makes them have 'the runs' even more. He is in his early sixties, and I know he has lots of experience, but I feel he is wrong on this matter.

At the moment he has a dog, and after each run (only trials so far) the dog seems to be panting excessively and flops right out afterwards. He seems to be very distressed after the trial. This is the only time the dog has fresh water to drink. Please could you advise who is right and who is wrong on this issue?

TRAINER'S TIP

The degree of dehydration can be estimated by a skin pinch test over the neck, shoulder or flank area. A slow return of the skin indicates dehydration or reduced body fluid reserves, often caused by travelling, hot weather, barking in the kennels, or excessive nerves in greyhounds. A supplement of physiological electrolytes should be given, with access to cool, clean water or rehydration fluid.

A In years gone by, there was a common belief that if a greyhound drank a lot of water it would not race as well. This myth is no longer widely respected. In warmer weather in particular, it is most important that a greyhound be provided with a supply of clean, fresh drinking water at all times. This is because as a greyhound pants, water vapour is evaporated from the lung surface to aid in the cooling. The thirst response is triggered by the increase in body salt levels in the blood and the greyhound would normally drink to replace lost fluids.

If the greyhound is denied water, generally it will become dehydrated and not perform. Lack of water also concentrates the urine excessively, and in order to restrict loss from the body, the greyhound can develop bladder and kidney problems. These include crystals in the urine, and more chance of kidney damage from the effects of fast galloping and the build-up of acids in the system. Although many dogs like to drink cabbage water, it may contain toxic chemicals that can affect iodine levels in the greyhound's body and then cause metabolic problems, and a loss of performance. Although extra water can be given to greyhounds by adding it to the food so that they take it in when eating, it is generally important to provide cool water for a greyhound to drink at all times.

There is still a lot of controversy about giving water to greyhounds with diarrhoea. It is most important, obviously, to replace the fluids lost by diarrhoea to avoid dehydration. However, excess will make the gut contents more fluid, and perhaps prolong the diarrhoea. In this case, it is best to give an electrolyte fluid so that salts and water are taken in to replace salts lost in the diarrhoea. Trainers often find it is better to give the greyhound small amounts of fluid and electrolytes frequently, rather than allow the greyhound with diarrhoea to drink excess amounts of water.

Obviously if the greyhound is suffering from dehydration, then electrolytes and water should be provided, and in severe cases, the vet may have to give fluids into the vein. The typical symptoms of panting excessively and collapse after racing are quite often due to a fluid and electrolyte imbalance leading to dehydration. Dehydrated dogs are unable to pant off water vapour to cool themselves quickly, and therefore tend to become stressed after racing.

It is probably best to provide water at all times when dogs are kennelled, particularly when electrolyte supplements, such as Betacel, are given in the feed. In the event of the greyhound drinking excessive amounts, then water should be provided in small amounts on a regular basis to control the drinking habit. In greyhounds that develop 'racing thirst' after a hard race, then withdrawal of water for a short time with continual assessment of the greyhound's dehydration state, is helpful in overcoming racing thirst. However, you should seek advice from your vet before withdrawing access to water completely.

Greyhounds that have access to outside areas during warmer months should be provided with water in a shady spot to keep it cool. Greyhounds tend to drink much more water when it is cool and fresh than when it is warm from standing in the sun.

FOOD ALLERGY

Q I recently lost my four-year-old pet greyhound, who died from what my vet diagnosed **51.** as a severe food allergy. The dog was in good health when I bedded him down, but when I awoke in the morning the floor where he sleeps was covered in vomit and diarrhoea containing a large amount of blood. I took him to my vet who gave him an injection to stop the vomiting. He diagnosed a severe food allergy.

After taking him home the vomiting continued, and he was taken back to my vet, where he stayed for a week before going into a coma and then dying from kidney failure.

I am still bewildered as to what he ate to cause his death, and it was also upsetting that it took him a week to die. Could you please shed some light on what it could have been that he ate (or what food is known to cause problems for greyhounds), and is there anything that could have been done in aiding his recovery?

A Sudden death can be associated with poisoning, heart problems and even parvovirus infection in greyhounds. Acute infection with parvovirus in a non-vaccinated greyhound can cause vomiting, as you describe, and diarrhoea within 24 hours. The greyhound would normally have a high temperature and severe depression.

From your description it appears that the greyhound could also have taken a substance that causes severe diarrhoea, vomiting and blood loss. In many cases this could be products such as snail baits, or even a carcass of a small animal, e.g. a rat poisoned with rat bait. Obviously your vet would have investigated or recognised these symptoms of poisoning.

As far as food allergy is concerned, the only allergy that I have seen in greyhounds is red meat allergy to high levels of beef, mutton and horse meat. It seems that some families in line breeds of greyhounds are unable to digest red meat sufficiently, and this can upset their system in the form of a food allergy. However, generally it causes low grade diarrhoea rather than sudden poisoning. Generally, changing the greyhound to chicken meat, fish or a diet of dry food and rice, etc. will settle down this type of low grade food allergy.

If your pet greyhound had been eating table scraps, then a high dose of salt or even an allergy to shellfish could have caused his symptoms. However, I suggest that you think about the type of foods that your greyhound could have got in the period immediately prior to his digestive upset, or whether your greyhound had access to the outside street area before he developed the symptoms.

As far as treatment to aid his recovery, then the primary cause of the condition is unknown at this time. Therefore, it is difficult to give any advice on the actual supportive therapy that could have been used to aid his recovery. However, from the symptoms that you have described it appears to be a case of misadventure or poisoning.

Chapter Three

LAMENESS

PADS

52. Q I have a greyhound bitch, aged four years, and for the past nine months I have been trying to get her back on the track. The trouble is behind her front wrist; the stopper pad splits open and starts to bleed, and it takes about five to six weeks for it to fully recover. Then every time I trial her over a 300 yd sprint it opens up again. If I let her run in the fields and run about with her kennelmate it does not open up.

It all started when she ran out of a field on to a concrete road and she split it open then. It sounds as though it was my fault, but she jumped a high wall chasing a magpie.

A Unfortunately, without surgery, splits on stopper pads do not heal properly to withstand the rigours of racing. Therefore, I would suggest that you take the bitch to your vet for surgery. In most cases, the vet will open up the wound and scrape the edges. It is best to leave the wound to heal as an open wound, taking care to keep it clean and bandaged. This allows the wound to stretch as it heals, and with controlled walking, the skin repairs to allow elasticity without tearing as the greyhound gallops.

It may also be worthwhile having the stopper X-rayed, in case there is a small piece of foreign matter in the area which could be interfering with the healing of the wound.

53. Q What is an efficient preventative and curative treatment against hard pads?

A I assume you refer to the excessive drying and cracking of the margins of the pad which expose the underlying soft tissue. This is most commonly due to drying out of the pad due to exercise on road surfaces, dry sand tracks, and during warm weather. The moisture in the skin is lost, and the surface of the pads dries out and cracks.

In most cases, regular daily applications of a pad preparation to moisturise and condition the pads is very effective. A product such as Padaid Cream is recommended. It should be applied prior to walking on dry roadways or sand, and then re-applied once the dog returns. In some cases, an individual dog may have exceptionally dry pads on all four feet. In this instance it is sometimes

BONE (SKELETAL) STRUCTURE
OF THE GREYHOUND

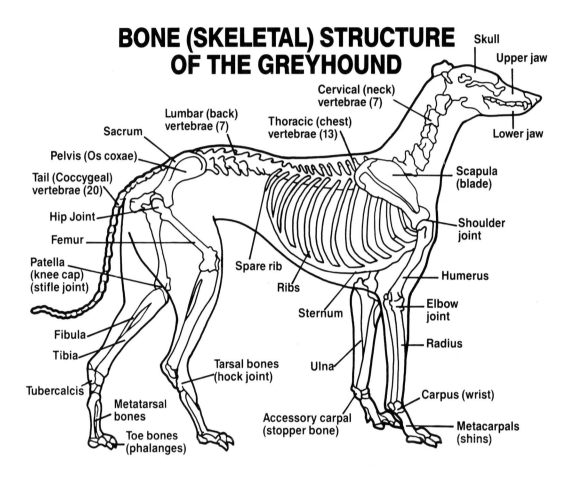

beneficial to provide a piece of carpet smeared daily with a light coating of neatsfoot oil (oil from cow hooves) and nail it to the floor in the kennel or run where the dog stands during the day. Neatsfoot oil is relatively bitter, and is not licked off as quickly as Vaseline, mutton fat, etc. However, it does make a mess of bedding and the kennel area, and only a small amount should be brushed on to the carpet.

Some dogs that have been affected by the distemper virus develop hardened pads and thickened skin on their noses. If this is the case, the only treatment is to provide neatsfoot oil and Padaid Cream as regularly as required, to help soften and keep the pads pliable.

In other instances, a condition commonly called 'foot rot' occurs in the pads and webs and eventually the toes. The pads become very thickened and cracked into the underlying surface. This condition is usually caused by leaching oils from the skin, or by either very wet or very dry soil, allowing fungal organisms to invade the underlying surface. In some cases applications of neatsfoot oil overnight, and Padaid Quick Heal morning and evening, are helpful in controlling the infection and softening the pads. In severe cases it is best to seek veterinary advice for treatment. A course of antibiotics, anti-fungal agents and iodine preparations need to be applied for up to three to four weeks to get the best results.

IMPORTANT MUSCLES OF THE GREYHOUND

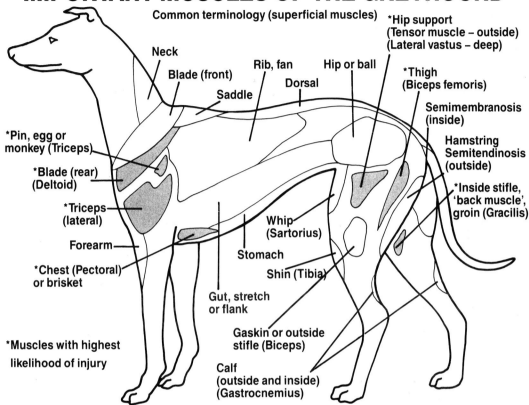

Common terminology (superficial muscles)

*Hip support
(Tensor muscle – outside)
(Lateral vastus – deep)

Neck

Blade (front)

Rib, fan

Dorsal

Saddle

Hip or ball

*Thigh
(Biceps femoris)

Semimembranosis
(inside)

Hamstring
Semitendinosis
(outside)

*Pin, egg or
monkey (Triceps)

*Blade (rear)
(Deltoid)

*Triceps
(lateral)

Forearm

*Chest (Pectoral)
or brisket

*Inside stifle,
'back muscle',
groin (Gracilis)

Whip
(Sartorius)

Stomach

Shin (Tibia)

Gut, stretch
or flank

*Muscles with highest
likelihood of injury

Gaskin or outside
stifle (Biceps)

Calf
(outside and inside)
(Gastrocnemius)

Q Year in, year out, we have greyhounds lame on the front feet. I rack my brain trying **54.** to figure out why. The pads look perfect. Where have the dogs been walking? Could it be something they have eaten? Is it their age? I have seen other breeds in this town being walked out limping on one or both of the front feet, and I have spoken to the owners and they have excuses like age, rheumatism, "it's the breed" etc. This happens around the same time every year when the council are out with their sprays, which is the only thing that coincides with this lameness.

The weed spraying is done with a paraquat chemical called Gramoxo W. A council worker who used to do this, told me they are supposed to dilute the chemical at about 40:1, but they spray it at even-mix to save doing the job again.

I have taken my greyhounds to various vets over the years telling them my theory, but it seems to go in one ear and out the other. I have given vitamin E, vitamin B1, and the last vet said that one greyhound had an old shoulder injury which has tightened up. I do believe I am right with my theory, but no one listens. The dogs do recover from it, but it takes time. Is there an antidote for this lameness or not?

A   Although there has been no documented evidence on the absorption of paraquat weedacide causing lameness in dogs or other animals, there are some side-effects associated with the concentrated form of the chemical. Studies have shown that concentrated forms of paraquat can cause dermatitis in humans and other animals.

In most cases this causes pain and swelling of the skin, and peeling of the skin, where concentrated chemical comes in contact with it. It is only slowly absorbed through the skin, and therefore does not show any signs of toxicity unless it is spilled on the skin in large amounts. It can also cause damage to the nails, but again, this is only associated with the concentrated from of the chemical. When sprayed on weeds, paraquat is taken into the plant and fairly quickly broken down in the environment. Therefore, unless you walked a greyhound on the newly sprayed surface, there would be very little chance of it causing a dermatitis or other damage to the pads. Such a reaction to the chemicals would normally cause inflammation of the skin between the pads or webbing, and associated lameness. From your description, you mention that there is no outward sign of soreness or skin problems in the feet.

I suggest that you contact the makers of the product, ICI, and discuss your findings with them. Alternatively, I suggest you carry out a small field trial of your own. Perhaps you could walk some greyhounds on the grass verges and others on the footpath and see whether dogs walking where the chemical has been sprayed show signs of the lameness you describe?

There are a lot of other conditions that can cause intermittent lameness in greyhounds. The most common is insufficient calcium in a diet which can cause bone weaknesses and stress leading to recurring lameness. However, these dogs commonly break down in races and suffer from joint and bone problems. I suggest you take your worst affected greyhound to a greyhound specialist vet for a thorough examination. I am unaware of any antidote for this type of lameness, but I would be interested in any new information you gather on the association of paraquat chemical and lameness in greyhounds.

55. Q   Two months ago my three-year-old graded dog sustained a hock injury during a race. Examination by the vet revealed no bone injury and he diagnosed a severe strain. The treatment given was a local cortisone injection and advice to rest for two weeks. I returned the dog to his quarters where he was rested, and given short but frequent visits to his small paddock to empty himself.

After ten days the hock had greatly improved; he was walking well and was able to undertake light exercise on a lead. He exhibited no signs of discomfort. At this point this hitherto excellent kenneller, with perfect feet, began gnawing at the pads on all four feet. This behaviour has become habitual and the results disastrous, with large areas of pad completely removed exposing raw areas.

The hock injury is now apparently completely repaired and his general health is excellent. The dog has always had a relaxed and placid temperament and this has not changed. I have made extensive inquiries but nobody has been able to give any explanation as to the cause of this distressing trait. I do not believe in muzzling the dog 24 hours a day, and keeping the feet covered permanently with dressings is not a practical solution.

A   It is not uncommon for greyhounds that are confined to kennels due to injury to develop behavioural problems. In most cases, eating manure is the most common vice that greyhounds develop when kennelled for long periods. However, licking the paws can also result from boredom.

Generally greyhounds do not gnaw at their pads in the way you describe. In most cases this type of self-mutilation is started, or aggravated, by irritation to the pads. This is commonly due to concentrated disinfectants, new cement kennel surfaces, or something irritant in the bedding. In this case the webbing and soft tissues around the pads will show evidence of being irritated and inflamed. Generally, the only way to prevent dogs from licking their feet excessively is to cover them with a light bandage. Applications of bitter substances, including neatsfoot oil, or human products containing bitrex to prevent thumb-sucking in children, may discourage the habit.

Unfortunately, in severe cases you may have to muzzle a dog for long periods during the day. If possible, take the dog for regular walks to reduce boredom and take his mind off chewing his pads. Other old remedies include the application of vinegar, citronella oil, and aloes wiped or sprayed on to the feet.

Q **I would be grateful if you could advise me on a problem I have with my greyhound's foot. The dog races on a sand track and always comes off with a small sandburn in exactly the same place – in the palm of the foot of the off hind leg. The problem was made worse when a friend suggested I use a silver nitrate caustic pencil on the open wound, which I did, and to my horror the next day the sandburn, which was usually the size of a matchstick, had opened up to about 1/2 inch long and 1/4 inch wide, and had burnt quite deeply into his foot.** **56.**

I have spent a month healing this up fully, but I have been told it will probably open up again when I run him next. Therefore, is there anything you can suggest I put on his foot to try and toughen it up before I race him again?

A Sandrash or sandburn can be quite a problem in some racing greyhounds. The abrasive sand particles lacerate the skin beside the toes, or the skin and margin beside the main back pad. Often the wound begins to weep, and if not managed correctly, will increase in size and cause lameness. Usually sandburn cuts are very slow to heal because the skin is so fine.

Unfortunately, the use of caustic substances such as silver nitrate pencils often burn the sensitive skin and make the wound worse. The abrasions are more common on coarse tracks during wet weather. Therefore, the best method to avoid it recurring is to change tracks or avoid galloping the dog on a coarse sand wet track.

I have found a couple of treatments that are useful in helping to heal up sand rash. The product Granuflex, available from your veterinary surgeon or greyhound supplier, is particularly useful for treating lacerations in the pad. Apply a coating twice daily for at least a week, then once daily thereafter until the wound heals over. Vitamin A cream, available from a chemist, is also useful to help increase the healing rate of the skin. However, both preparations should be cleaned off before galloping the dog on sand as the sand will accumulate on the skin and cause further irritation.

Another product, Riko Spray, is a commercial form of Friars Balsam, which is also useful to spray on before walking the greyhound. For open wounds, it is best to protect them in a sock or stocking when taking the greyhound for a walk. Once the lesion is healed up the skin can be hardened by applying such preparations as Padaid Paint or Padaid Quick Heal at least once a day, or more frequently during wet weather.

These products will also help reduce the risk of infection in the area, as well as prevent excessive softening of the skin during wet weather. I have found that these treatments are useful to prevent the condition recurring. However, as mentioned above, try to avoid hand slipping or galloping the dog on a coarse sand track during wet weather.

57.Q I recently took my blue-coloured 22-month-old bitch to a local vet to see what treatment she could recommend for my bitch's badly cracked pads. The edges of the pads are very fibrous, crusty and cracked, and her stoppers are just the same, resembling the head of a cauliflower with rough pointed fibres.

The bitch has not done a lot of racing to date, and she has never been lame after racing on sand and grass tracks. The vet said there is no treatment she could recommend, as these rough fibrous cracks are something the bitch is producing herself and they are not through to the flesh. However, they look and feel so bad that I feel they must affect her racing soon. I hope you can help or advise me on this complaint.

A It is not uncommon for bitches, in particular, to suffer from fibrous crusty edges to their pads and stoppers. Some authorities claim that it is due to a hormone imbalance, particularly in cases where the bitch's skin is generally dry and flaky. However, it may simply be a case of dried out pads.

It is best treated by applying a suitable moisturising agent each day. For example, regular applications of a product such as Padaid Cream will help to moisturise and condition the pads and make them soft and supple. Products such as petroleum jelly or mutton fat are also useful, but greyhounds often lick these off soon after they are applied. In severe cases a piece of carpet smeared with neatsfoot oil can be nailed to the floor where the bitch frequently stands in the kennel or run. This will apply a light coating of oil to the pads and help to keep them in good pliable condition.

There is another condition, commonly called foot rot, that initially starts with dried out edges to the pads. This is a progressive type of condition that firstly affects the pads, then the webbing, and eventually the whole foot below the wrist. Pads can become grossly thickened and cracked into the underlying tissue, which usually makes the dog extremely lame. The skin is thickened, reddened and looks angry, although it remains dry and hard. It is caused by leeching of the oils from the pads, usually as a result of very damp conditions, or alternatively very dry soil which draws the oil from the pads. This allows a fungus organism to invade the pad tissue and this progressively spreads over the pads and feet.

Greyhounds with pink skin are more commonly affected, although it can occur in other dogs including blue greyhounds such as your bitch. Treatment for foot rot must be thorough and regular. If the bitch becomes lame, you should consult your vet for advice and specific treatment. In mild cases, applications of neatsfoot oil or Padaid Cream will help to control the condition. In other cases the application of a human product for treating tinea, or an iodine based wash such as Betadine, is suitable and may need to be applied for 14-21 days at least.

Other specific treatments need to be given if the condition does not clear up within two to three weeks. The greyhound must be housed on clean, dry surfaces and bedding must be changed daily. It may also be worthwhile putting the bitch on a supplement that contains vitamin A, such as Feramo-Greyhound, or tablets to give 3000iu of vitamin A daily. Vitamin A is helpful in treating dry skin and skin conditions in general, and may help heal up dry and cracked skin.

58.Q My two-year-old bitch recently produced a rather large corn on her front pad. There was no visible sign, only the fact she was very lame. After a close examination we found it was her pad which was sore and after a long haul with a vet, she had it cut out under anaesthetic.

As you can imagine, she carried her foot for a long time – six weeks in all – until the wound had healed. I am pleased to tell you it has now healed completely, but on occasions she tends to carry it. I believe it is just habit as there is no sign of pain when touched.

After all this, I find she is getting another one on her back pad. It is not as big as the previous one, but I don't want to go through all that again. I have heard you can get laser treatment. Could you tell me if this is so, and is it expensive? If you cannot use this treatment, are there any other remedies to get rid of corns or to prevent them; she does seem prone to them. I don't give her a lot of road work – about 1/4 of a mile a day, and then she is allowed to run freely.

A Corns consist of hard lumps of pad, which can slowly grow to cover the whole pad surface. The corn develops its own blood supply and has a very deep base set in the underlying tissues of the foot. Obviously, the surgery performed by your vet was very successful, and is usually the best method of treatment to prevent re-growth of the corn. Generally, corns are more common in greyhounds with white feet and pink pads. Applications of human preparations for treating corns are not usually successful in the greyhound. However, they may help to delay the development of a small corn.

As far as laser treatment is concerned, there have been many claims made for this type of treatment in treating corns and other injuries. Laser treatment is usually found to be useful in the early stages of a corn. Once the corn develops its own blood supply and is firmly attached to the underlying tissues, there is a lot less chance that laser treatment will be of benefit. This treatment is not expensive, particularly where there is a course of treatment given over a period of time. Your own vet would be able to give you advice on where to obtain treatment in your area and the likely expense.

There are no hard and fast remedies for treating corns. Many trainers claim that certain lines of greyhounds are more prone to them, but there are no proper records to suggest this relationship. I would suggest that you try laser therapy as, theoretically, it would be more beneficial than the normal treatments for corns that are available. However, in the long term, if the corn fails to respond to laser therapy, the best treatment is to have them removed surgically by your vet.

If your bitch has very soft pads, I would suggest that you try a drying preparation each day to harden up the pads and prevent bruising of the underlying tissues which may form the focus for a developing corn. Avoid walking her for long distances on hard road surfaces, and try to ensure her training gallops and hand slips are run on grass or soft track surfaces.

NAILS

Q I would be grateful if you would advise me about a greyhound dog with brittle **59.** toenails. He is two and a half years old, and I have had him for five months since purchasing him in a sale. He had one toenail missing from the front toe, left leg.

When I raced him he came off with the shell of the toenail missing from the right leg. After seven weeks I gave him a trial, and this time he came off with two toenails missing – one off each hind leg. They just seem to snap off. I keep the toenails as short as I can. He always seems to do it at the first bend.

A From your description, the nails appear to be pulling out from the nail-bed under the cuticle. Brittle nails usually snap off, or split, without pulling away to expose the underlying nail bone. Brittle nails can be treated by giving the dog a course of methionine,

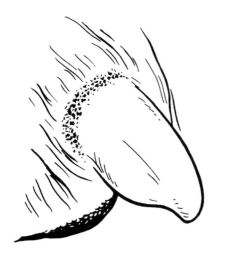

SORE QUICKS
(Sand Toe)

CRUSTY EXUDATE
CAUSE: Abrasion and lacerations of cuticles, sand impaction when galloping, low-grade persistent bacterial infection of trapped sand. Greyhounds with white feet or toes more susceptible. Wet weather softens skin and cuticles. The outside and inside toes on the hind paws most commonly affected. At the gallop, the cuticle separates from nail and flares out to allow more sand to be impacted. Sand on tracks and dirty kennel environment also infect cuticles with bacterial germs and fungus. Swelling and pain may result in discomfort and lameness which reduce performance.
TESTS: Examine outside and inside toes on hind limbs for inflamed or enlarged cuticles. Gently squeeze to check for infection and degree of pain.
MANAGEMENT: Gently wash out sand with running water. (Hose or wash off the feet after each gallop). A soft bristle brush is helpful to remove impacted sand – a toothpick may assist. Deeply ingrained sand may need to be removed by a Veterinary Surgeon. If quicks are sore and inflamed, seek Veterinary advice.

such as 2-3 Methnine-90 tablets daily for four to six weeks, and ensuring the dog is on a calcium supplement. Calcium is required for the strength of the nail, and a daily supplement of a calcium powder will help increase the strength and prevent nails breaking off.

External preparations used by women to harden their nails are also useful in some cases. A supplement of the B complex Biotin, about 1-2mg daily in the feed, is also used to increase the quality of the nail in dogs. Biotin is available as a powder for horses, or as tablets from human health food shops. Nails that chip off on the ends can be hardened by the application of a coating of epoxy glue, which is allowed to set and then rounded off with a small file.

However, in your case, if the nails are pulling out completely, then it is most likely due to chronic infection with bacteria or fungus in the nail-bed, or sore quicks due to sand. In this case, treatment with an effective antiseptic and healing preparation is helpful. The product, Padaid Quick Heal, is recommended for treating skin/nail bed-infections and pulled nails.

If the nail roots appear to be infected then you should seek advice from your vet, as a course of oral antibiotics may be necessary to clear up the infection. Keep the nails and feet as clean as possible to avoid infection, and keep them as dry as possible by changing the bedding frequently. A hammock-type bed is often helpful in keeping the bedding dry.

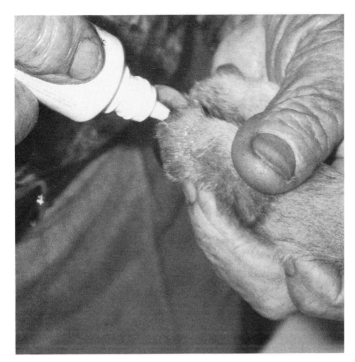

Sore quicks can be caused by abrasion and collection of sand when galloping, and are more common in greyhounds with white toes. After carefully cleaning the sand out with a cotton bud, or irrigating with a stream of water to flush out the sand, antiseptic and healing lotions will help treat infected cuticles and quicks. These are more easily applied by lifting the foot and positioning the delivery tip on the side of the nail, just in front of the inflamed cuticle. Deposit a drop or two of lotion and allow it to run down the nail and under the cuticle by capillary action.

60. Q I have an 18-month-old greyhound and he is an outstanding prospect, but he has had broken nails on at least five occasions, partly shelled or partly snapped off, revealing the quicks. I have also had trouble with him dehydrating after racing. I have cured that by giving him Slow K the day before racing, as well as vitamin C. I also give him glucose in his pre-race meal. I am wondering if there is any possible connection between the two complaints?

I feed him wholemeal biscuits, vegetables and meat – tripe, chicken and beef. He also gets fish, cod-liver oil and linseed oil. Just recently, I have given him black pudding and daily calcium tablets. As I say, I can control the dehydration, but I want to find out more about it and whether there is any connection with the nails problem.

A Broken nails can be caused by a number of conditions, but generally it is due to a weakness in the nail structure. The treatment you are giving to control the dehydration seems to be adequate, but I would suggest that you chip the Slow K tablets before feeding. This is because they are covered with a hard coating, designed for absorption from the small bowel in humans. Greyhounds have a shorter length small bowel, and in many cases, the Slow K tablets are not fully dissolved in the area of the bowel where potassium is absorbed.

Therefore, it is best to chip a small piece out of the Slow K tablet with a spoon to allow it to break down more quickly in the small bowel. This will give the greatest benefit to the greyhound and help ensure that the dehydration problem is corrected. It may also be necessary to give your dog a supplement such as Betacel to ensure his electrolyte levels are balanced and that he has sufficient reserve for racing.

As regards the nail problem, I would suggest that you ensure the dog has adequate levels of calcium in his diet. Normally, greyhounds require anything from 5-7g of calcium to balance meat-based diets. Adding 2-3 small calcium tablets per day would not prove adequate to balance the diet. Furthermore, calcium is an important component in the structure that bonds the nails together, and a lack of calcium in the diet can result in weakened nail structure, and the increased incidence of shelly or broken nails.

A B complex vitamin, biotin, has been used for treating brittle and shelly hooves in horses. Some greyhound trainers have reported that the addition of a small quantity of biotin, about 1-2mg per day, seems to be helpful in increasing the growth rate and resilience of the nails. You should be able to obtain a biotin supplement tablet made for humans from your local chemist or veterinary surgeon. Other supplements, such as Calci-D, containing calcium, are recommended for greyhounds to provide adequate levels of calcium to balance the meat based diets. Biotin is also found in higher quantities in raw egg-yolks, and some trainers believe that feeding two raw egg yolks per day can be useful in strengthening brittle nails. However, you must ensure that only the raw yolk is used, and the whites of the egg are separated from the yolk as they contain an anti-vitamin that will bind up and make biotin itself unavailable to the greyhound. Alternatively, lightly cook the eggs to destroy this anti-vitamin in the whites.

In many cases addition of the amino acid methionine to the diet also helps to improve nail quality. This is best done by giving 2-3 Methnine 90 tablets per day in the feed to provide this important amino acid for strength and growth of the nails. If the nails are splitting and feathering at the ends, they can be protected by applying an epoxy type glue to the end and allowing it to harden to form a protective coat. Your hardware shop would be able to advise you on a suitable type of glue to put on the end of the nails to protect them. You should choose a glue that hardens quickly. It is best to clean the ends of the nails with methylated spirits, dry off and apply the glue to the end. Keep the dog on a table until the glue is hard and provides a protective coating. The glue can then be lightly filed to remove any sharp edges and protect the ends of the nails.

If the nails are being pulled out at the nail junction, it may be that the dog has an infection in the nail quick area. This can be controlled by applications of a product such as Padaid Quick Heal, which has been specially developed for sore quicks and sand toe. It helps heal the quicks rapidly, and controls any infection in the nail-bed junction. In some cases, the rate of nail growth can be increased by massage of the cuticle areas with a light application of a counter-irritant substance, such as MR Iodised Oil. This can be applied to the area above the quicks each day and lightly massaged on the affected toes. This has the effect of increasing blood flow to the tissue that secretes nail, and can be useful in helping the nails regrow more quickly. I suggest that you discuss this aspect with your vet.

61. Q A greyhound I purchased had an infection in one of his nails on his hind foot. My vet recommended that the nail should be removed, as the infection had gone deep. Having had the nail removed, the toe has healed up very well. The problem is now hardening the area. After leaving the dog off the track for eight weeks he still skins the area and goes lame. I have tried permanganate of potash. My father recommended that I tried boiling oak bark and putting his foot in this solution daily, but to no avail.

A In many cases this is the best course of action to clean up a persistent infection. However, when the toenail is removed, the pointed end of the last bone in the toe is left under the skin surface. This should be protected until the new nail grows. The only successful treatment for this type of condition is to have your veterinary surgeon remove the end joint of the toe, thus removing the sharp piece of toe bone that is under the pad.

The treatment you have already tried will help to harden the nail and skin of the pads. Daily applications of a product such as Quick Heal will dry and harden the skin, and prevent further infection. In greyhounds, where the end of newly grown nails are soft, coating with an epoxy glue and allowing it to dry, then filing off to shape with a nail file is the best way to prevent the nail point breaking off. Alternatively, use a nail hardening product made for women's nails.

Q I have a black four-year-old greyhound bitch. About four months ago she came off the track from racing and had lost three toenails, and at least two had lifted from the quick. I took her to my local vet who prescribed tablets for paramite. I gave her two daily, and I laid her off racing for seven weeks. During this time, her nails all came off, but new ones grew. I thought she must be cured, but now I have noticed that the nails are starting to lift.

62.

I give her good food. Her diet is cooked meat, Wafcol biscuit, plenty of fresh vegetables and brown bread. She has raw eggs, Weetabix, glucose, honey and cod-liver oil on her dinner two to three times a week. When getting her ready for racing I give her a good tonic, Cytacon Vitamin B12. The bitch seems to be very lively otherwise.

A In most cases, loss of the toenails is associated with infection in the nail bed. However, greyhounds that have suffered some severe type of sickness, particularly kidney or liver damage, may also develop a fault in their nail growth and the nails become more brittle and are shed more easily. From your description it certainly appears to be a condition commonly known as fungus nail. In bad cases the nails will actually deviate and deform to cause problems when the bitch is galloped. As the new nails grow, they tend to be thicker and much shorter.

In most cases, treatment for such a condition usually takes six to twelve weeks, depending on the severity and type of fungus or germ infection. Besides giving the dog some type of antibiotic to control any bacterial infection under the nails, daily applications of a product such as Padaid Quick Heal should be applied to the nails to help control the fungus infection under the quick. Continue this therapy daily for at least four to six weeks to ensure that the new nail growth is not hampered by the recurrence of the fungal or bacterial infection. Once the new nails have grown, after four to six weeks, the bitch can be walked.

It is important to keep the nails well trimmed and the bitch housed on a dry bed, and avoid walking or kennelling the bitch in damp or muddy areas. Although you may lose the next growth of nail in the same way, prompt and long term treatment with antibiotics will help control the condition with time. The diet you are giving her could be slightly imbalanced, as the amino acid methionine which is essential for nail growth, is deteriorated by cooking meat. Therefore, it would be best to add a supplement of methionine, such as 2 Methnine 90 tablets daily to her food, to give her adequate levels of this important amino acid for growth of the nail.

As you are also feeding raw eggs, biotin in the diet, which is an essential vitamin in the diet for growth of the nail, may be destroyed as well. You must cook the egg whites to inactivate the substance that destroys biotin in eggs. However, you may continue feeding raw egg yolks without any effect on the level of biotin. Supplements of biotin, a B complex vitamin, are available generally from health food shops, and you may wish to put your greyhound on a dose of 1.0mg of biotin each day in the feed to encourage nail re-growth and strength of the nail.

TOE INJURIES

63. Q Unfortunately, my bitch has had to have a web removed. Since then, every time she runs, the very bottom of the V splits slightly, as if it is a cold hack. After very slight bleeding, it takes about two weeks to heal up again. Therefore, every time the dog runs she is not 100 per cent fit, having been off for three to four weeks.

I was wondering if there would be any possibility of stopping this splitting or at least getting two or three consecutive runs, or am I wasting my time?

A Basically, the strength of the web is maintained by a thin ribbon of tissue at the front border. If this band of tissue is torn or removed, there is less strength in the web to hold it during running. The toes themselves spread to the maximum distance allowed by the webs during running. In severe cases, the web needs to be removed, as was necessary in your bitch.

However, in many cases, if insufficient web is removed, it only tends to split at the point where the webbing is stretched to its maximum during galloping. In this case the webbing tears each time the dog is galloped, and it develops into a chronic injury, which forces the greyhound to be rested

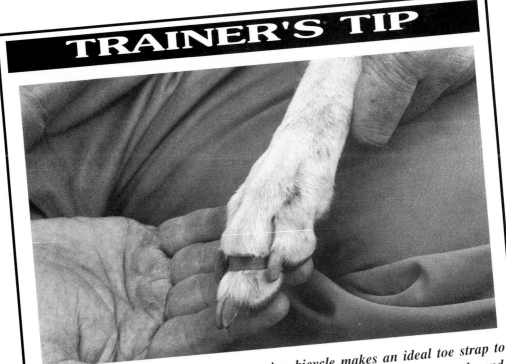

TRAINER'S TIP

A small band of inner tube from a racing bicycle makes an ideal toe strap to support an injured toe when walking, handslipping and trialing a greyhound. The ideal band is approx. 1.5cm diameter, and 5-6mm wide.

up for long periods between each race. Normally, the dog should not be galloped for at least six to eight weeks after the webbing has been repaired in this way.

I suggest you carefully spread the toes on each side of the area, and test whether the webbing is under stress and therefore likely to split. In this case, it may be worth talking to your veterinary surgeon about having slightly more webbing removed to overcome this problem. This will allow the toes to spread and avoid tension on the webbing area. Leave the area as an open wound. Keep it clean and apply an antibiotic/antiseptic preparation to prevent infection. Bandage to prevent contamination, and walk the greyhound to encourage the wound to stretch as it heals. I have found that the application of an ointment containing vitamin A helps to heal the skin and strengthen the weak area. Other products are available from your veterinary surgeon for helping to soften scar tissue and make it more pliable.

During trialling and training gallops, some trainers prevent the toes from splitting by applying a rubber band or tape around the toes on each side of the injured area. However, in most cases dogs do not require this type of support. I suggest that you contact your vet on advice on taping the toes for trials etc.

If the split area appears slightly infected, it would be necessary to treat the infection. In this case,

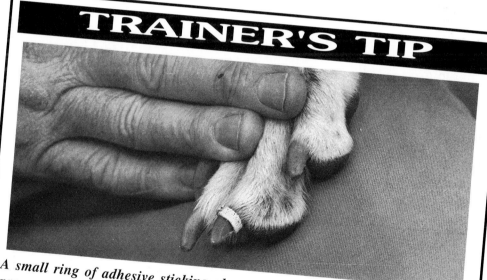

A small ring of adhesive sticking plaster makes an ideal deflector "rim" to prevent sand being forced up the nail and under the cuticle (quick) during galloping. Simply form a small section of sticking plastic into a small tube about 2mm diameter, (sticky side out most). Carefully stick to the outside toenails about 2mm in front of the hairline, encircling and overlapping it by 2mm at the top side to prevent it being dislodged when the greyhound gallops. Alternatively, a small "O" ring or latex band used on human teeth, is also easily applied and very effective.

regular applications of a product such as Padaid Paint or Quick Heal may help to control any infection and harden the area so that it heals.

I hope that the above suggestions are of help in stopping the web splitting each time your bitch gallops. In most cases, once the webbing heals sufficiently the splits do not recur.

64. Q **My 22-month-old bitch puppy has split the centre web on each of her front feet while in the traps during only her third trial. She had been showing a lot of promise, having won her first trial, finishing runner-up in the second and winning the third trial in which she split her webs. I have since had the webs trimmed back and stitched.**

My problem is that, apart from the three trials mentioned, there is no previous form to compare against when she returns to racing. I have no way of telling whether this injury has handicapped her future career. In your experience, have you found that this injury seriously affects a dog's speed and agility?

A In my experience, provided the webs heal satisfactorily, there should be no real long term effect on the greyhound's speed and performance. However, if the webs fail to heal adequately and risk splitting open again during galloping, then obviously this will affect her performance. From your description, she seems to have plenty of ability and hopefully the injury will not affect her in any way.

65. Q **I went over to Ireland to pick up my puppy of thirteen weeks. I have schooled him, then I started to trial him. I found he was very keen and clawing at the front of the traps to get out, resulting in him splitting his middle web. I took the dog up to a vet who specialises in racing greyhounds, and he stitched the web.**

I brought the dog home, and let him rest for six weeks to give it a chance to heal. I then trialled him again – and he split both front webs. I took the dog back to the vet, who cut them back and stitched them again, and said I was very unlucky that this recurred. I will not trial the dog again until they are completely healed.

I wondered if there is any kind of bandage/plaster that can be used on the web. I am very happy with the puppy as he is keen and alert, but I am beginning to wonder if he will ever race, let alone win. I hope you can shine some light on the matter.

A When the webbing between the central toes is torn, it usually needs to be removed and sutured as carried out by your vet. Whilst there is a much reduced chance of the webbing tearing apart again, the two central toes are likely to spread excessively during galloping, causing soreness and other problems in the toe joints.

In most cases, it is best to strap these two toes together, using either a 1/2 inch wide elastic adhesive tape, or preferably a thick elastic band. In most cases a rubber band made from cutting a 1/2 inch wide cross section of a cycle racing tube is satisfactory when slipped over the first joints of the two central toes to keep them together when the dog is galloping. This can be applied when the greyhound is hand slipped or trialled, and it may be worthwhile seeking approval from racing authorities for use on the greyhound when it is racing. In practice, where the webbing on the outer toes is torn, then a double layer of a 1/2 inch wide adhesive bandage stuck to the hair and wrapped around the upper toe area of all the toes on the foot is useful to help prevent excessive spreading out of the toes when the greyhound is galloping. In my experience, once the toes are kept together in this way the greyhound can race without risk of further injury.

Foot injuries can be caused when a greyhound claws at the front of the trap, as it waits to be released.

Q I would be very grateful if you could help me in solving a problem about my brindle bitch, who is nearly two years old. When she was 19 months old she broke a toe on her right hind foot while racing. I took her to the local greyhound vet, who removed the first joint of the toe. A week after the toe had been removed she came into season, so she has had a good rest of about 14 weeks.

I have recently started to exercise her again with steady road-work and a few hand-slips in the local football field. This is where the problem lies! While running with her at jogging pace she has a tendency to carry the affected leg for two to maybe six paces at a time. This is affecting her racing as, when she tries to lift her leg, she finds it difficult, resulting in short strides and an uneven action, although this does not happen all the time.

When handling the leg for signs of disorder, she shows no response or reaction.

66.

A The removal of a broken or sprung toe usually offers a quick and permanent treatment, with little or no loss of performance. Your bitch has certainly had sufficient time to recover from the surgery and allow repair of the injury.

In many cases, you will find that the toe will be sore after the first two or three exercise runs or during the first week or two of road-work. Soreness can usually be treated by applying a topical anti-inflammatory cream containing a pain-killing drug such as phenylbutazone. This would normally be available from your veterinary surgeon.

However, in a small number of cases, greyhounds still continue to show soreness despite no obvious problem with healing or infection. Some trainers believe that it is in the greyhound's head,

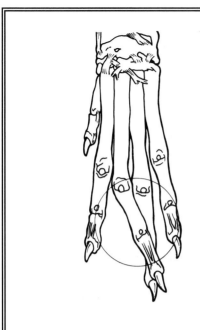

SPRUNG TOES

CAUSE: Partial or complete rupture of the collateral ligaments joining the toe bones.
TEST: Twist toe to side. A 45 degree bend indicates collateral ligament rupture, only 90 degree bend indicates complete joint rupture.
FIRST AID: Strap injured toe to adjacent toe if possible, then apply a padded bandage to foot.
MANAGEMENT: Seek veterinary advice as soon as possible.

but this is not the case. It is due to an increased sensitivity of the amputated end of the toe bone and surrounding skin. Again, it will require treatment by your vet.

This involves injecting a substance that causes increased scar tissue formation at the end of the amputated toe, confining the dog to a kennel for five to seven days, and applying an ice pack twice daily for ten minutes each day. In most cases the soreness will disappear within ten to fourteen days. If the soreness still remains, the procedure can be repeated.

67.Q My 16-month-old puppy has an injury to his third toe, right front, diagnosed as a loose first joint. The vet states that there is a gap where the nail hits the joint; she suggests removal of the first joint. However, a respected NGRC trainer states that the joint should not be removed because of the strain the other toes will be under, especially as she is so young.

Will a rest help to make the joint stronger or will it have to come off? Suggested rest is six weeks. Incidentally, the pup has raced once and won, and is very good.

A From your description it sounds like simple sprain of the ligaments that hold the toe joint together. This is generally described as a loose joint, rather than a typical sprung toe where the lower bone can be deviated to the side. It is also not uncommon in young dogs to develop a fracture of the middle bone, and thus X-rays are useful to help differentiate between a fracture and a typical sprung toe.

However, from your description it appears to be a simple case of ligament strain. Generally, massage with a linament, such as MR Iodised Oil, for two to three minutes twice a day for seven to ten days will help to cause tissue reaction in the area which will strengthen and shorten the ligament. After this time the greyhound can be walked on a lead for ten to fourteen days, without

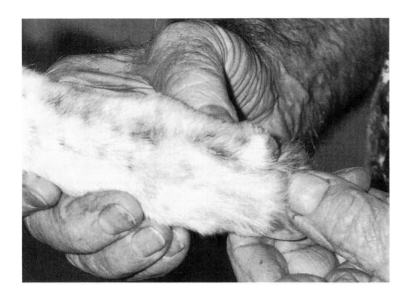

This greyhound has had the end joint of the inside toe removed after the toe was severely torn when galloping. The pad has been relocated and wrapped over the end of the stump to protect it when galloping.

Example of a dislocated or "sprung toe" with swelling and pain in the second joint. Check toenail length by standing the animal on a table – toenails should just touch the table surface. This greyhound previously had long toenails which can increase the risk of the injury and pulled out nails when galloping on a grass surface.

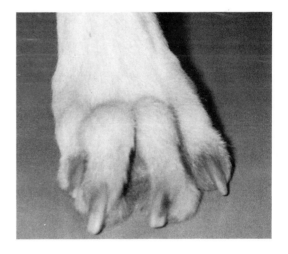

galloping, and then allowed to run over a short distance of 100-150 metres on a straight track daily for a week or so. This helps to strengthen the toe, and in many cases, the greyhound can be back on the track within four to six weeks.

The ligaments around the joint can also be injected by your vet to increase the healing scar tissue reaction, and this may be useful in helping to reduce the healing time. It is important to make sure the nail is kept short on the affected toe to prevent catching on the track as the dog gallops.

Q **My dog recently broke the number three toe on his off-hind. The toe had to be removed two joints back. A friend of mine, who has had dogs for many years, says that this is the worst possible toe to break and it will affect the dog at bends. Is this true? Can you explain why the vet removed the toe halfway between joints?** **68.**

A   Removal of the toe usually has very little effect on the greyhound's overall performance. However, it depends on the length of the toe removed, as to whether the greyhound has problems with the 'stump' of the toe. If a 'stump' of bone is left when the toe is removed between the joints, the greyhound can 'stub' the toe during galloping. This can lead to laceration of the skin over the retained piece of bone, and lameness. In this case it is best to remove the toe at the joint and round-off the end of the joint rather than to cut the toe halfway between each joint. However, your vet may have had a reason for removing the toe halfway between the joints.

I would suggest that you keep a regular check on the end of the first toe bone that is left, and if the greyhound appears to be bruising and lacerating the end of the stump, then you may have to have some or all of it removed. Generally, it is best to round off the end of the bone that forms the joint to allow the pad to cushion the bone and provide support when the greyhound is galloping. I suggest that you contact your vet again if you suspect the greyhound is stubbing the stump when galloping.

69. Q   **My greyhound recently injured one of the small tendons in the area between the toes and the wrist. I know little about these sorts of injuries. A friend who examined the dog felt some slight swelling and said that I should ask a vet to remove the tendon.**

When I explained this to another friend, he reckoned that there was no need to remove tendons. He said that regular massage with a good embrocation would soon put the matter right. I am confused as to which course I should take. Could you please help?

A   These tendons are vital for the proper action of the toes, and can become sprained when they are stretched beyond their normal limits during racing, or when a greyhound is forced off course during a gallop. There is no need to surgically remove the tendons, as this would interfere with the proper action of the toes unless the lower end of the tendon that attaches to the toes is affected. In this case it would need examination by your veterinary surgeon to determine whether the toe is affected, and thus the lower end of the toe may need to be removed.

However, for a simple tendon strain as you have described, then massage with a linament as you suggested, laser therapy over the area, magnetic field therapy and even ultrasound applications over the area, may help to strengthen the tendon and aid repair. If the area is swollen and painful initially, then ice packs applied for one to two minutes two or three times a day will help to reduce the swelling pain which, if left untreated, can affect the long term healing of the tendons.

It is also worthwhile to ensure the greyhound is on a feed supplement containing vitamin A, such as 4g Feramo-Greyhound each day, as this may help to strengthen the healing tendon. Your suggestion of massaging with a good embrocation would be the initial treatment for this type of injury. If it does not respond to the therapy and remains swollen and sore, then I would seek specialist advice from your veterinary surgeon.

WRIST INJURIES

70. Q   **I have recently acquired a three-and-a-half-year-old bitch. The problem with her is that after she has raced she develops a limp, and her right front wrist is sore when examined. Ten minutes after the race the limp has gone, and the next day she is jumping about in her kennel ready to go out. Her previous owner thinks she did it jumping over a fence.**

My local vet is not interested in greyhounds and I cannot seem to find a good greyhound vet in my area. Could you give me any advice on the wrist? I know of a couple of dog men who have Magnetopulse machines but are not sure how to treat wrists.

A From your description, the bitch appears to have a strain in the ligaments in her right front wrist. It is unlikely to be a bony problem as she appears to recover fairly quickly after a race. It is important to have your dog thoroughly examined by a greyhound vet to ensure she is not carrying an injury in her shoulder or spine that may make her transfer more weight onto the wrist when galloping.

The wrist should also be thoroughly examined by a vet to determine the degree of flexion and the extent of pain on flexion. If the bitch cannot flex her wrist almost double, then there is a possibility that she has some ligament tears or even arthritis in the joint. In some cases, an X-ray might be required to determine any internal joint problem.

TRAINER'S TIP

Doubling over or backward flexion of the wrist is a simple test for wrist mobility in a racing greyhound. Any injury, soreness, or swelling within the wrist area will cause discomfort and lameness when the wrist is flexed for about 30 seconds, and the greyhound trotted off on a loose lead. Consult your vet for advice if the greyhound favours the limb after a flexion test. This simple flexion, hold, then trot off test, can be carried out on any other joint (eg. shoulder, elbow or hock) where soreness is suspected.

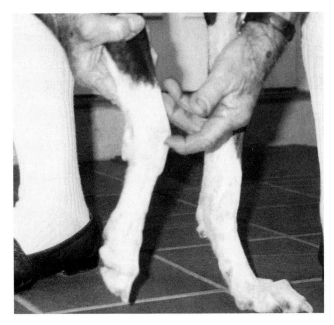

Wrist injuries can cause a greyhound to lose lengths when racing, and are often caused by internal tearing of ligaments within the wrist. Swelling may not become apparent until the day after the race. Consult your vet for treatment advice.

As far as therapy is concerned, it is important to determine the underlying reason for the wrist soreness. Magnetopulse machines are certainly valuable in treating muscle injuries and other bony conditions of the joints. Normally, ten minutes' therapy twice daily would be beneficial over a two to three week period. Treatment with a muscle linament such as MR Iodised Oil may be helpful in reducing the pain and inflammation in the joint. It is unwise to use an ultrasound machine over the wrist bones, as it may cause damage to the bone. However, massage with Iodised Oil and a combination of magnetopulse may be helpful in settling down low grade ligament sprains in the wrist. The exact treatment should be determined by a greyhound veterinarian. I suggest you contact your local greyhound track or other trainers for reference.

71. Q I am writing to you about my dog, bought in Eire, and costing quite a lot of money. I have had him for nine weeks and he is a really good dog – the fastest starter I have seen. But he does not seem to take the bends as he should.

Six weeks ago he was in the semi-final of a £2,000 open race. He trapped out and was 3 lengths in the lead at the first bend. The following dog passed and went 3 lengths into the lead. When my dog straightened up he was only beaten by 1/2 length. There is nothing dodgy about this dog as he has won nine open races, some by quite a distance in good times.

I have had examined by a vet, who diagnosed necrosis in a bone in the wrist. He told me to run him only in sprints at ten-day intervals and apply ice packs after his races. I informed the man who sold him to me and he said to lay him off for three months. Is there anything that can be done for this dog? Should he be rested for three months or ten days? The X-ray showed minute specks of bone in the wrist.

A It appears from your descriptions that if there are chips of bone visible on X-ray, then the dog is suffering from an osteoarthritis condition of the wrist. Unfortunately, this can become a chronic long term reason for lameness. But with proper care and treatment the

To check for a free forward stride, place thumb and hand over point of shoulder and extend leg forward to check for tightness and pain.

dog may be able to race quite successfully if his races are spaced out and therapy is applied to the wrist. Obviously, the shorter, faster races would be better for him, as the wrist pain would increase in longer races, as he puts more stress for a longer duration on the joint.

It is also a good idea to have your vet examine the greyhound's lower thoracic spinal area, in case an injury makes him transfer more weight on to the wrists when galloping. A greyhound with a deep groove between the shoulder blades is often carrying a back injury which tends to alter the galloping balance, particularly as the greyhound corners.

Depending on the degree of damage to a joint, an injection with a product containing hyaluronic acid such as Hylartil Vet, administered by your vet, could help to repair the damaged joint. This is particularly so if inflammation and signs of osteoarthritis are present. Normally greyhounds treated in this way should be rested for three to four weeks, and many greyhounds return to work with little evidence of bone damage.

Radiation of the wrist, by a qualified registered veterinarian for applying radiation therapy, could be useful in helping to minimise the bone fragments in the wrist. Swimming the greyhound for one to two minutes, twice a week, will help to maintain heart and lung fitness without weight on his wrists. Alternatively, an injection into the wrist with a long-acting cortisone injection, with adequate rest of three to six weeks following the injection, may be useful in helping to settle down the inflammation. However, further damage to the wrist may occur following cortisone injection, but it may be helpful in allowing the dog to race successfully every fourteen days for some time.

I would suggest that you give the dog at least ten to fourteen days between races if you can, to allow the wrist to settle down. The application of ice packs after racing would be helpful, and also some type of linament, such as MR Iodised Oil, to relieve the inflammation and pain.

A product called Dermcusal is widely used overseas for treating arthritis in wrists of greyhounds. It is not currently available in England, but I understand it is available in Ireland. Dermcusal is useful in helping to reduce arthritis in damaged joints. I am sure that with some type of therapy and adequate rest intervals between races, the dog should be able to race successfully.

72. Q I have been given a three-year-old greyhound bitch. She sprained a wrist in June. The previous owner had a final X-ray taken nine weeks after the initial injury, which shows damaged ligaments at the back of the wrist. As a consequence, bone is growing there. Apparently, because of this, his vet has doubts about her racing again and cannot advise any treatment other than a long rest.

Would you explain this bone formation please, and why it should be seen as a problem. For the dog's sake, I would love to see her racing again. Can you please suggest a course of treatment or exercise programme that would strengthen the wrist for eventual racing?

A From your description, it appears that the bitch has pulled some of the internal ligaments at the back of her joint, either inside the wrist that connects the rows of bone together to form the wrist joint, or at the back where the tendon joins on to the accessory carpal bone and stopper area.

Where the injury results in tearing of the ligaments from their bony attachment, a bony lump will develop as the bone and tendon try to heal and re-attach. If the injury is outside the actual wrist joint, then the best form of treatment is long term rest, and perhaps therapy such as magnetic field or laser therapy to increase the rate of healing of the damaged ligament or tendon in the area.

A supplement of 2500-3000iu of vitamin A daily, such as contained in a 4g dose of Feramo-Greyhound, would be beneficial. Application of a muscle linament or other counter-irritant

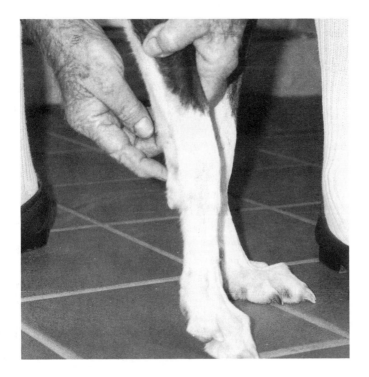

If the greyhound fails to stretch out during a race, and pulls up favouring one front limb, check for injury to the stopper and accessory carpal bone by squeezing over and around the stopper behind the wrist. Consult your vet for treatment advice.

embrocation would be useful to increase blood flow in the area, which in turn may aid the healing in the ligament and tendon areas.

If the X-ray shows that internal surfaces of the joints themselves have undergone degenerative changes, then in some ways this may be more easily reversed and have a much greater chance of the bitch returning to racing than if the major tendon attaching behind the joint is torn. Again, your veterinary surgeon would be able to advise on the types of treatment available for internal damage to the wrist.

Common treatments include injections with products such as Hylartil-V, low dose corticosteroids, and other substances that help to repair the joint surface. Therefore, the location of the bony changes on X-rays would determine the type of treatment, and also the exercise programme.

If the external tendon bone attachment is the underlying problem, then exercise by walking on the lead over a period of two to three months, increasing to a light trot over 200-300 yards each day, and ice packing the tendon area for one to two minutes, with an ice pack on return from this walk each day, would help to strengthen and reduce the inflammation in the tendon area. This, combined with a vitamin A supplement as mentioned above, and a suitable counter-irritant or embrocation type linament, would be useful to help the healing process.

As a general rule, if bone re-growth is present then this normally signifies a more chronic form of injury and there is usually less chance that the greyhound will return to the racetrack. In years gone by, radiation therapy to restrict the bone growth was popular, but again your vet would be best qualified to advise on available therapies after the X-rayed changes have been taken into account.

Q **I have a dog with a severe wrist problem. The injury occurred some time ago and it is now a permanent weakness. Providing that we keep him to sprints and do not race him more than once every ten days, he just about stays sound.** **73.**
Although it is hot after racing, we hose the wrist down and he walks sound on it within 48 hours. Is there any other treatment, e.g. ultrasound, that will help his condition? Secondly, since it is difficult to keep him fit, would swimming help?

A Unfortunately, once a greyhound sprains the wrist then it usually takes some time to heal, particularly if ligaments inside the wrists are sprained. Most internal sprains of the wrist usually end up causing arthritic problems, with long term weakness and reduced flexion.

Exercising and galloping the greyhound over short sprints to keep him fit, and racing him every 10-14 days should help to settle down the condition and allow the wrist to strengthen. A layer of elastic bandage over the wrist may also be helpful to give extra support for galloping.

Application of cold water or even ice after a race is important to relieve some of the pain and swelling. Applying an ice pack twice a day for one to two minutes for two to three days after each race would be helpful. However, do not ice the wrist immediately before exercise, as this will reduce flexion and increase the risk of damage to the joint. It would be better to warm the joint up, using a linament or magnetic field therapy before galloping.

General treatment can include massage with a product such as MR Iodised Oil to provide some warming effect to the joint. Although ultrasound therapy is useful, it is probably best done under water so that it reduces the risk of damaging the bony areas of the wrist, immediately under the skin. However, if you are going to use ultrasound under water, it is probably best to seek advice from your vet or a registered physiotherapist. The ultrasound head must be fully sealed against

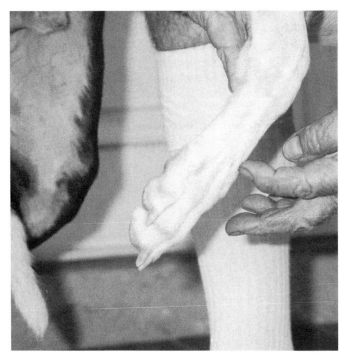

Swelling and pain over the metacarpal (shin) bones develops in young greyhounds that are trialled or galloped around end circles on racetracks. These small bones have to remodel to withstand the extra bending forces when cornering, and if this overloading is introduced by galloping around end circles too fast in early trialling and racing, metacarpal soreness may develop. Pressure applied with the thumb and index fingers by sliding down the length of each metacarpal on the front feet, will cause discomfort in your greyhounds whose shin bones are not adapting to circle gallops.

water, and proper time and method used to avoid damage to the wrist. One of the most common treatments that is effective is the use of magnetic field therapy on the wrist, once or twice a day, which will help to warm the wrist up and possibly aid healing.

As far as swimming is concerned, it certainly will take weight off the wrist and reduce the strain on the wrist structures, but still enable the greyhound to exercise. Swimming will help keep a greyhound fit in the lungs and heart, but it will not condition the greyhound for racing. Therefore, short sprints and then swimming for two to three minutes maximum, every second or third day, would be useful to help maintain fitness and reduce the strain in the wrist.

74. Q **I have a six-month-old dog puppy, whose offside foreleg is bent back at the wrist joint so that the stopper pad is low to the ground. This condition has only become apparent these last couple of weeks. It is as though the tendons in the back of the leg have little support. The dog has not injured himself, and it does not seem to be painful.**

Of course, it is very ungainly. The other leg is normal, and his litter mates are OK. I wonder, have you seen this before? Will it correct itself as the dog grows? Is there anything to be done, or can nothing be done?

A It appears that the greyhound was born with a limb deviation that was either not noticed early on in life, or has become worse as the dog has grown. In many cases this is due to some sort of development abnormality in the young pup, with structural weakness in the joint and tendon area.

If the condition has not improved over the last six months, then it is unlikely the dog will be a racing proposition. However, I would suggest that you obtain an opinion from your own vet as regards the possible cause of the condition. It could be that the greyhound has had an interruption to the 'bone growth plate' above the wrist area on that particular leg, caused by either an injury – a rickets-type condition where the puppy lacks calcium for some reason (he may not be able to absorb it adequately) – or even malformation prior to birth. Because the condition is not painful, it suggests that it is a malformation and he is the 'unlucky' one in his litter.

I suggest that there is probably little that can be done at this stage, but an opinion from a veterinary surgeon should be sought, and X-rays may be able to define whether there are any internal joint problems or collapse of the joint that could lead to this type of limb deviation.

Q **There seems to be a new drug on the market that is used to help wrist injuries. 75. Unfortunately, I do not know any brand names though I understand it is similar to, but better than, cortisone. It is injected into the wrist and apparently is imported from Australia. Can you help?**

A The product that you have heard about is called Anarthron D. It is available in Australia as you mentioned, and has been shown to be useful in treating wrist and other joint injuries in racing greyhounds. It is particularly useful in treating joint conditions where joint cartilage has been injured, eroded away or diseased.

In early cases only one injection needs to be given into the joint. However, in joints where the cartilage is badly eroded, then repeat injections at weekly intervals are recommended. The dog should be rested for three to four weeks after the last treatment to allow the joint to repair. Following that time, a further three-week period of graded walking exercise is required before the dog returns to work.

The treatment has a direct benefit in helping to repair the joint. It also helps to reduce inflammation and soreness in the joint. Unfortunately, cortisone injected into the joint really only reduces the soreness and inflammation, but with rest the joint itself may repair after some time. However, cortisone injections can increase the risk of bony changes inside the joint, and this can lead to further long term arthritis. Your vet would be able to explain the difference between the two types of treatment.

I am not aware that the product would be licensed for use by veterinary surgeons in Britain. Perhaps your own vet could make enquiries as to the availability and licence for use of this product.

Q **I have a dog with a severe wrist injury. My local vet showed me the X-rays, and 76. although nothing is nothing broken, the dog has been left with a weakness in the off-fore.**

Many years ago I used to go to a London vet who would ring-fire the wrists in similar condition. When I asked my local vet if ring-firing would help this dog, he said he wouldn't consider it and that it was going to be banned. Is it banned yet? If so, why? I know that this treatment was carried out successfully on a number of racing greyhounds.

A In years gone by, pin-firing the skin area over the wrists and metacarpals in young greyhounds with 'shin soreness' was a common treatment carried out to strengthen the subcutaneous tissues and cause reaction over the area, which was considered to aid the healing process. Pin and line-firing was commonly applied for similar injuries in racehorses.

However, studies in 1983 at the University of Bristol suggested that pin-firing had no benefit to

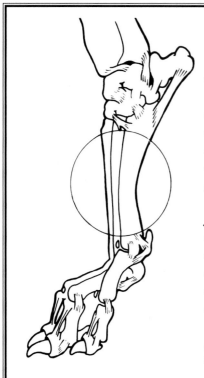

SHIN SORENESS

(Metacarpal Stress)

CAUSE: Develops due to bone stress and concussion usually as a result of galloping young greyhounds on circle tracks, particularly where tracks are hard, and poorly maintained tracks with loose sand on bends. Causes lameness. Risk of fracture in severe cases. Often overlooked as a cause of poor performance in young greyhounds.

TEST: Press firmly on each metacarpal bone on the front legs. Heat swelling, or bone change (roughening of surface) may be present on the outside two "shins" of the left (near) foreleg, and inside two "shins" of the right (off) foreleg.

MANAGEMENT: Severe cases – seek veterinary advice as soon as possible. Mild cases – After 2 weeks of walking exercise, the greyhound should be galloped on a straight run or track for 2-3 runs. Consult your Veterinary Surgeon.

healing of tendons and ligaments, when compared to other less invasive treatments and rest for bony and ligament injuries in horses. For humane reasons, it was officially discouraged as a treatment for sprains, strains and racetrack injuries.

In greyhounds, as a treatment for the type of injury that you describe, many trainers consider ring-firing has a benefit when combined with rest and support of the injured joint. In some countries, veterinarians still use it for joint and ligament injuries.

I would suggest that you try other treatments, such as magnetic field therapy, combined with massage using linaments, and support bandaging of the joint when galloping. Wrist support pads are available and are quite useful in this type of injury. If there is no internal damage, then rest for two to three months will often help settle down the injury as well.

If the injury is recurring, then I suggest you have your vet check the spinal column behind the shoulder area for abnormalities, as they can sometimes cause more stress to be placed on the wrists.

SHOULDER INJURIES

77.Q I have a four-year-old greyhound, who races once a week. After his last five races he has shown to be lame on the left shoulder the next day. After examining the dog and looking for signs of pain during these examinations, I am unable to detect any injury. The problem is that after a day's rest he shows no sign of lameness, nor is he losing form in

MUSCLE INJURIES

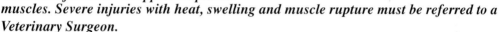

CAUSES: Extreme racing stress, sudden change in speed or direction due to interference, checks or falls, accumulated "wear and tear" of racing. Minor muscle injuries may be aggravated by continued racing if not detected early.

TESTS: Carefully examine individual muscles with thumb and forefinger to detect heat, swelling tensing of surrounding muscles, cording, a squelchy feel (haemorrhage), tears in muscle sheath, gaps in muscle fibres or "dropped" ruptured muscles. Severe injuries with heat, swelling and muscle rupture must be referred to a Veterinary Surgeon.

FIRST AID: If soreness, swelling, haemorrhage or tears are detected apply a cold pack for 3-5 minutes. Repeat every 10-15 minutes in severe cases and seek veterinary advice. Dropped muscles – gently push muscle back in place, apply a cold pack and bandage firmly – seek immediate veterinary attention.

MANAGEMENT: Treatment depends on degree and type of muscle injury. NOTE: Apply cold therapy for 5 minutes 3-4 times daily for first 24-48 hours of muscle tears or haemorrhage. Do not massage or apply heating therapy to torn muscle areas for 3-4 days. Consult a Veterinary Surgeon.

Minor muscle injury – reduce to walking exercise on lead only for 3-4 days. Do not gallop. A gallop over 200-300 metres after 4-5 days may aid healing and strengthen muscles. Physiotherapy twice daily with pulsed hydrotherapy, ultrasound therapy, laser or magnetic field therapy may be beneficial in more serious injuries. Ensure the injury has healed before greyhound is galloped. Consult a Veterinary Surgeon for advice.

Serious muscle injury – requires surgical repair, physiotherapy and controlled exercise. Consult your Veterinary Surgeon.

running. Are these symptoms common in a dog of this age or could there be an injury problem?

A In most cases, problems in the shoulder originate in the shoulder joint itself, the muscles surrounding the shoulder blade, or the muscles in the lower part of the neck. From your description, you have thoroughly examined the muscles, and can find no obvious injury. Generally, even a minor injury to the muscles of the shoulder will cause the dog to lose form and show signs of soreness when examined.

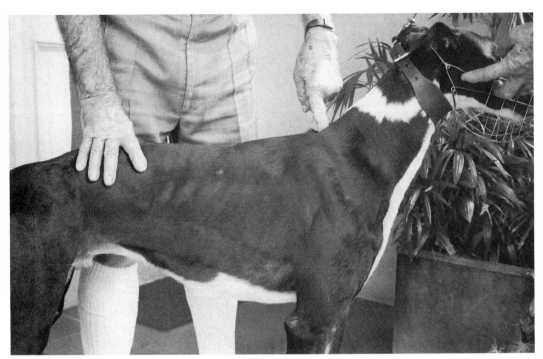

Finger pressure applied over the midline at the lower neck will help pinpoint a common area of soreness in a greyhound that gallops with its head held higher than normal. Also check the lumbo-sacral area by squeezing with the arched hand over the pin bones, as the neck injury can lead to secondary lower back pain. Greyhounds with sore backs due to cramping, react to squeeze pressure along the top back muscles.

At times, slight arthritis in the shoulder joint itself, which would be a possibility in older greyhounds such as yours, could cause an intermittent lameness which would not affect the dog once he is warmed up and galloping, but may show up for one or two days after a race. However, you would normally be able to pinpoint the soreness to the should joint if you examine the dog after the day of the race.

Occasionally, greyhounds develop soreness in the sesamoid bones or wrist, which can sometimes appear to originate in the shoulder. Therefore, it is important to thoroughly examine the complete leg when checking your dog over after a race. I would suggest that you have your dog thoroughly examined by a veterinary surgeon when he is showing signs of the lameness, such as the day after a race. If the problem is a mild arthritis in the shoulder joint, then treatment may only be necessary once it affects the dog's performance.

In younger dogs, degeneration of the cartilage in the shoulder joint can occur due to rapid growth and racing the dog at too early an age. However, in older dogs this type of degeneration has not been reported. If you decide that it is due to mild muscle soreness, then I suggest that you massage the dog twice a day for two or three days after each race with a produce such as MR Iodised Oil or muscle linament.

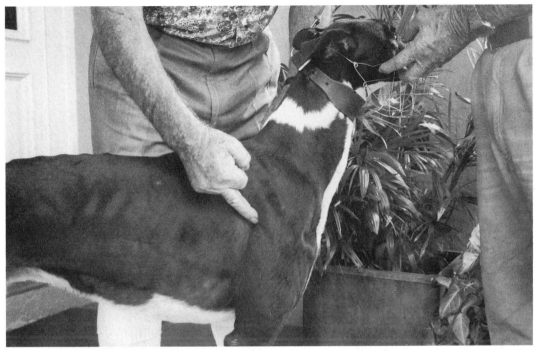

The point of the finger pin points a common area of soreness in the upper triceps area, which should be carefully examined on each side in a greyhound that deviates to the rail when cornering. Consult your vet for treatment advice.

Q I have a four-and-a-half-year-old dog. Four weeks ago he sprained a shoulder muscle **78.** in racing at my local track. The vet checked the dog and recommended a fortnight's rest. My trainer gave the dog three weeks rest. On the fourth week we gave him a couple of gallops to exercise him.

Within a few minutes a large lump came up on the dog's shoulder. This turned out to be a burst blood vessel, diagnosed by the vet. He has subsequently recommended four weeks rest, using the trainer's discretion as to when to bring the dog back into training.

It seems that bursting a blood vessel is quite rare in a greyhound. Could you please give me more information on this condition as I don't want to risk this recurring by bringing him back too soon. The dog has no history of this complaint or any muscle injury.

A It is very uncommon for a blood vessel to rupture in the shoulder of a racing greyhound. However, there may have been other tearing or bruising around the area of the original injury which weakened the blood vessel walls. You did not describe whether the blood vessel was a surface vessel or a deep vessel, with the shoulder muscles themselves.

It is not uncommon for areas of torn muscle to bleed immediately after the injury. This is usually felt as a sort of 'squelchy' spot at the site of the muscle injury, but this usually settles down within 5-7 days and heals without further recurrence. In some cases, treating the injury area too early with ultrasonic therapy can delay the healing of injured or burst minor blood vessels, which can recur

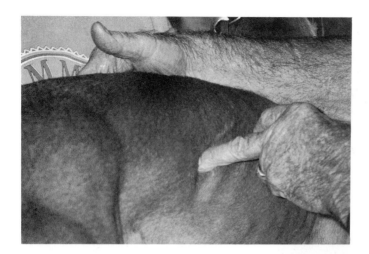

Soreness over the "spare rib" area can restrict stretching and speed. Surgical removal of the small last rib is popular, and in many cases greyhounds are back racing within 3-4 weeks with improved speed and performance.

Squeezing the lower triceps often causes discomfort in a greyhound that fails to stretch out and lower its head when running in a straight line.

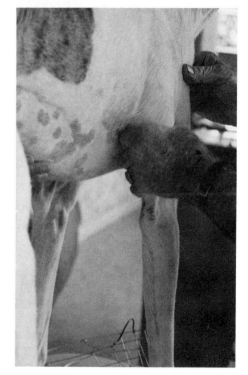

when the greyhound is galloped before the injury has had time to repair. Following this recent injury to your greyhound, I would suggest a minimum of four weeks rest, and then a careful check by your veterinarian before allowing the dog to return to training. I would suggest that a minimum of one to two weeks walking and light exercise should be given before the greyhound is galloped at speed in a hand slip or trial.

Some authorities believe that supplements of vitamin C and vitamin A may help to aid healing

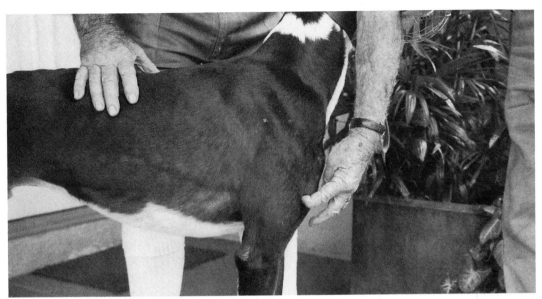

The finger pin points a common area of soreness where the triceps muscle joins onto the bone (radius) below the shoulder joint. Press with the index finger at the intersection where the two major shoulder muscles meet below the shoulder joint to determine soreness and degree of discomfort. Consult your vet for treatment advice.

processes and strengthen injured blood vessels. Therefore, a supplement of a product containing vitamin A, such as Feramo-Greyhound, and vitamin C, such as Rebound tablets, may be useful to help aid healing processes.

Q **I own a good open race sprinter, who recently came off with a shoulder injury. My 79. local vet could find no sign of muscle damage, but he reckoned the dog had just jarred himself.**

I don't understand the various muscle machines and lasers currently on the market, and, obviously, I would not know how to use them. Would there be any type of machine or laser that I could safely use on the dog? At the moment I am using a heat lamp twice a day and also massaging the shoulder with linament.

A For general injuries a magnetic therapy machine such as the Porta Mag 500 is probably the most popular, and can be used in various modes and times to treat muscle and other injuries. Because the whole greyhound is treated in a magnetic 'cage', much less hands-on time is taken to give treatments, particularly if you are busy.

However, some hands-on treatment is still important, such as initial heat lamp and hand massage with linaments over specific injury areas. I suggest you combine the best of both worlds with massage and magnetic therapy, as these two therapies are convenient and require less skill than ultrasonic treatments. However, ultrasonic treatment is helpful for deep massage of muscle injuries, and it may be more convenient to take your greyhound to a specialised physiotherapy clinic in this case.

HOCK INJURIES

80. Q I have a black greyhound bitch, who is a track record holder for 490m hurdles. I sent her for an open race, and she went over the second hurdle leading, but she landed badly and injured her hock. X-rays show there is no break, but there is quite a bit of movement in her hock although she is no longer lame. There was a bandage put on at the time, but not a plaster.

I will not run her over the hurdles again, but I would hope to race her on the flat. Do you think this is advisable?

A A sprain of the hock joint can lead the bitch to fracture in subsequent galloping. In most cases, sprain of the hock involves tearing or stretching of the ligaments around the front of the hock joint. The greyhound often only exhibits a slight lameness, with reaction to pain only when the hock joint is straightened. In other cases, the greyhound simply will not rest weight on that leg, and it is often put down to a bump or a knock.

If the bitch is allowed to race without time to heal, fracture of the hock can occur. In all cases of fractured hocks, the greyhound is lame immediately after the race, and many dogs have difficulty in completing the course. Surgery is often the only effective treatment for this type of hock injury, and usually results in the greyhound losing up to 1/2 a second in racing time. However, if the hock bones have a hairline crack, usually a bandage and restriction of movement for two to three weeks will be sufficient to heal them up. If the bones show a definite fracture line on X-ray, then a plaster cast for six weeks and rest for two to three months would be recommended.

This appears to be the case in your bitch. I would suggest at least a four to six weeks' rest from racing, and, if possible, use magnetic field therapy twice daily for two to three weeks to help repair the damaged joint. This will also help to heal the ligaments in and around the joint, particularly if you also massage the area twice daily for five minutes with linament such as MR Iodised Oil. Also ensure that the bitch is on an adequate level of calcium in the diet, such as 2-3 tsp of discalcium phosphate each day.

You are right not to allow her to run over hurdles again. Unfortunately, as severe hock injuries can make a greyhound lose a number of lengths, she may not be as competitive in her racing as she has been in the past. If your bitch continues to show intermittent lameness, or weakness in the hock area, I would suggest you contact your local veterinary surgeon for advice.

81. Q I have a 12-month-old puppy who is considered cow-hocked – how badly I am not sure. There are no obvious drawbacks to this, apart from looking rather splay-footed whilst standing still. I have read several publications on greyhound racing, most of which advise you to avoid the cow-hocked puppy, but they don't tell you why. Does this condition ultimately affect their racing ability? What causes it?

I would be grateful if you could enlighten me on this, as I know of one greyhound racing with this condition, albeit in low grade – is that significant? Can you get a fast cow-hocked greyhound?

A It is not uncommon for young pups to have cow hocks, and once they start to develop and strengthen during education and early training, quite often their cow hocks do not become so obvious. Certainly, if the pup is very badly cow-hocked, then it is more likely to affect its performance, and also risk injury to the hock joints when galloping, particularly around the

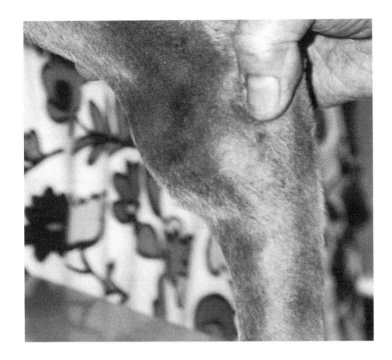

This photograph illustrates the swelling caused by a fracture ("popping") of the central tarsal (hock on the inside) bone due to badly maintained and poorly shaped and banked corners on a track. It is best to apply an ice pack for 3-5 minutes, then bandage firmly and seek advice from your vet.

bends in a track. However, good thing about cow-hocked greyhounds is that they do not knock themselves above the hock and develop a 'track leg' during galloping.

Generally, cow hocks are due to poor conformation as a result of genetic influences passed on by the stud dog or bitch, or in some cases a very badly balanced diet low in calcium with inadequate levels of vitamin D. It is important to ensure that all young greyhound pups are given adequate calcium in their diet, including a supplement of calcium powder, such as Calci-D. Unfortunately, milk does not contain enough calcium in the volumes that can be fed to provide adequate calcium for the growing pup.

In summary, you may find that the greyhound will start to straighten up more in his hocks once he starts regular galloping. If he was bred for his ability, then I am sure that he will show it on the race track. However, do not push him too hard too early, and allow him to develop fully before galloping, particularly if his hocks do look a little weak.

Q **I have a very good dog with a swollen hind leg around the hock area. The dog fell over and the inside of the hind leg muscle has a dark purple patch. I think this is a ruptured blood vessel.** **82.**
   Do you think the blood could have run down to the hock area? This swelling has been with him for over a week now, with no improvement. I have kept the dog on his bed all this time, only letting him out to empty, but the swelling has not gone down.

A From your description, it certainly does appear to be fluid (serum) that has collected around the hock from a broken blood vessel under the skin above the hock. Normally, this type of swelling is soft, with no lameness and the 'bag' of fluid can be distorted by pressing. However, you must ensure that the collection of fluid is not due to haemorrhage, resulting from a rupture or 'drop' of the 'back' or gracilis muscle in the inside leg. If you can feel a depression on the muscle layers above the bruised area, as compared with the same area on the opposite leg, then it is likely that a muscle has been torn or pulled from its attachment high up between the legs. If you find this type of injury, or you are in some doubt, you are advised to seek immediate advice from your vet.

As regards removing the fluid accumulated around the hock, it really depends on how much there is trapped under the skin. Small amounts, say 5-10ml, will probably reabsorb over five to seven days if the dog is walked for twenty minutes, morning and night. An ice-pack, or hosing cold water for ten minutes, may also help to remove any 'oedema' or 'pitting' swelling in the area.

However, if the bag of fluid is such that the hock is double its normal size, I suggest that you have the accumulated fluid drained by your vet under sterile hospital conditions. Do not attempt to drain it yourself, as it may become infected. It is unlikely to reabsorb fully, and could result in a permanent blemish to the hock, or restrict movement.

83. Q **I have a dog with a hock strain. Would this respond better using an ultrasound machine or a magnetic field machine, and which type of machine would you suggest is the best all-round one? Would you also please advise if I should use ice-packs, cold hosing or hot poultice, or both? Should I also use, say, Radian B or bone Radiol?**

A I assume you have had the greyhound examined by your vet and a diagnosis of strain of the hock has been given. In many cases where greyhounds have hock swelling or lameness, it is due to hairline fracture in the hock bones, and therefore other types of treatment need to be given. Generally, it is best to use a combination of massage with a product such as Radian B and magnetic field therapy to treat injuries involving the hock. Ultrasound machine type treatments are more beneficial in treating muscle injuries and soft tissue injuries rather than bony

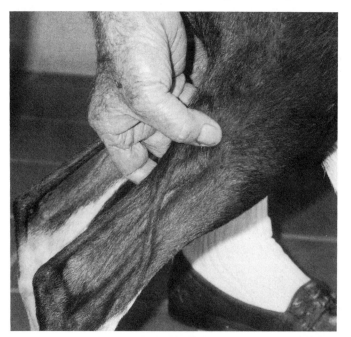

Strain and tearing of the lower area of the gastrocnemius muscle is relatively common in greyhounds that fall or are severely checked at the gallop. This injury should be suspected if a greyhound stands with one hind foot spread normally as it bears weight, and on the toes of the injured limb. The injured limb is favoured when walking and rested on the toes.

Injury to the hocks or swollen tendons in the front paw can cause a greyhound to slow up when cornering.

injuries where the ultrasound waves may actually irritate or damage the bone which is close to the skin.

Therefore, I would suggest that you massage in a suitable warming linament and apply magnetic field therapy twice daily to aid the healing of the strain of the hock ligaments. If the hock appears to be swollen, with increased fluid inside the joint, then you may need to seek further veterinary advice as other types of treatment may be more beneficial.

It is best to put a warm pack on the hock prior to exercising the dog to help warm the joint for exercise. After exercise, if the joint appears to be slightly swollen, than an ice-pack applied for 2-3 minutes may help to reduce inflammation around the hock and provide comfort. However, if the hock has an arthritic problem, ice-packs may only serve to stir the conditions up and result in more lameness. Therefore, treatment by massage, linaments and magnetic field would be the best and possibly the most beneficial way to treat a strain condition in the hock.

Q **Can you please help me with this problem dog. He is 18 months old; he is very fast 84. and never been led to the first bend. When he tries to go round the bend he loses all his pace, puts his tail up in the air and swings it about as if lame. But even running on the beach or when out walking his tail is still right up in the air.**

I took him to a good vet, and she said he had a little swelling on his hocks and a swollen tendon on a front paw. She thought that was the cause of the problem on the bends. But after a rest of three months he is exactly the same, but shows no injury after a race. One other dog out of the litter had a similar problem, but soon overcame this at about 14 months old. So, after a three-month break, could he still be green?

A There is no doubt that slight injury to the hocks or swollen tendons in the front paw could certainly cause the dog to slow up when cornering. However, I would expect that these problems would have settled down after the three months' rest period. It is correct that he may grow out of it as he gets older. However, your description of how his tail sticks up in the air and swings around when galloping suggests that the greyhound may have a lower spinal problem.

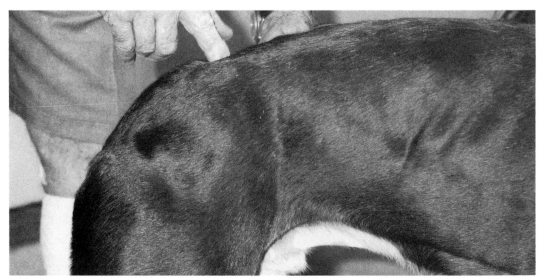

Lower back and lumbo-sacral soreness can be checked by pressing down with the index finger in the general area between the pin bones and the spine. Affected greyhounds often knock the track leg area, are slow from the traps, and throw out or "windmill" one back leg when galloping in a straight line.

Soreness of the lumbo-sacral joint ("coupling joint") area will cause a greyhound to jump poorly from the traps and wobble its rear end up the home straight in a race. This simple test to combine rearward manipulation of the hind leg with finger pressure on the spine centrally between the pin bones, will cause a pain reaction and signs of discomfort in greyhounds with "coupling joint" injury or arthritis.

Arthritis or injury to the lumbo-sacral joint can cause problems when cornering, and loss of coordination in the final stages of a race. In severe cases, the greyhound will feel pain and attempt to sit down when the back is pressed just in front of the pelvic pin bones.

Although the condition is not common in young dogs, it can occur as a result of fast growth or a fall during galloping. A thorough examination by your own vet may be able to pinpoint the problem in this area. In a young dog I also suggest that X-rays should be taken of the spine to ensure that there is no abnormality that has developed during growth. It seems odd that a litter mate had the same problem; it may be a family weakness in the area. It is most common in young dogs with a long coupling area between the ribs and pelvis, which normally suggests a weakness in the area.

Alternatively, I suggest that you train and gallop the dog on a straight track, and, initially, try to trial him on tracks with gradual bends, to help strengthen up the back and overcome the problem. However, if your vet is unable to find a back problem, then a thorough examination of the shoulders may also find an injury that is interfering with the dog's galloping action.

Q **I have taken my greyhound to two different vets. The first well-known greyhound vet** **85.**
examined the dog and diagnosed (without any X-ray) a hairline fracture of the hock.
He injected the hock and gave me some pain-killers for the dog and told me to run
him a week later, then take him back.

In the meantime I was worried that if we ran the dog with a hairline fracture it would
break. So I took him to my local vet for an X-ray, and he said there was no fracture of the
hock. The problem was in the hip. We have been treating the hip with ultrasound and laser
for seven weeks and we have not run him at all.

We returned to the first vet with the X-rays, but he still insists the hock is fractured, while
our local vet still says it is not. We would like your opinion on whether the dog has a
fractured hock or not, or if the trouble is in the hip. Having spent £50 and travelled 220
miles, we are none the wiser. The dog has never had any swelling on the hock. I enclose the
X-rays for you to examine.

A Unfortunately, it is sometimes difficult to make a definite diagnosis based on X-ray alone.
It is always helpful to examine the greyhound for signs of pain, swelling and tissue damage
to locate a possible site of the injury.

The X-rays of the hock fail to show any definite hairline fracture on the views that have been taken. However, there is some change to the lower part of the hock joint, with narrowing of the joint space and signs of bone change in the area. After seven weeks most hairline fractures would have healed up and left some arthritic change inside the joint.

I normally flex the joint up, and hold the leg off the ground for about one minute. Then trot the greyhound off immediately and observe any increased degree of lameness. If the greyhound exhibits discomfort only after the hock has been flexed, then one must consider some type of chronic arthritic damage to the hock joint.

On examination of the X-ray of the pelvic area, again, the X-rays fail to resolve anything of particular importance. However, there is some change to the actual ball and socket joint on one side of the hip joint, but this may not cause the greyhound any discomfort. In the area that is arrowed there may be some tearing of the ligaments that hold the pinbone area to the pelvis. However, this also could be confused with faeces and other material in the bowel overlaying the area. Again, a thorough examination of the area by deep finger examination would be

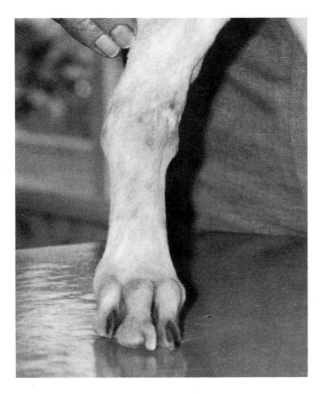

This photograph shows an example of a small boney lump (calleous) on the central tarsal bone from an earlier fracture. A cast was applied for 4 weeks, and kennel rest for another 6 weeks was given to heal the fracture. Always feel for a lump in this area when purchasing a greyhound as it is evidence of a previous hock injury.

recommended. The type of treatment that you have been giving over the rest period would be quite sufficient to heal any type of injury in this area. If the greyhound still shows discomfort and lameness on exercise, then I suggest that you have the greyhound examined thoroughly by a third veterinarian, preferably a racing greyhound specialist, for his opinion.

HIND LEG INJURIES

86. Q **My greyhound is two and a half years old, and he has a back leg stifle injury. My previous trainer recommends him being put down as he states the problem will just recur. But he is a good dog, and I feel that with today's advanced cures in veterinary surgery, something surely can be done. After all, dogs with broken hocks undergo surgery and win races again.**

A In both these conditions, it depends on the exact type of injury to the joint. In the stifle joint the most common injury occurs in young dogs, particularly large pups which are allowed excessive galloping early on in their life. Generally, after a few runs a pup appears to 'bunny-hop' or use both legs together.

In this case, the greyhound should be examined thoroughly by your veterinary surgeon. X-rays may be required to locate the injury, usually in the top of the bone below the stifle. In young dogs this type of injury can be repaired by surgery, and has no long-term effect on a dog's performance in racing. However, in the older dog, such as yours, injuries involving a joint often result in long term chronic joint arthritic and other problems, which can reduce a dog's performance.

MUSCLE WEAKNESS

(Lack of Stamina)

CAUSE: Inadequate training to build-up greyhound for stress of racing, or lack of fitness for distance, poor diets, heavy worm burdens, anaemia, lack of adequate Vitamin E in diet.

TESTS: Greyhound fails to "muscle up", and lacks stamina and strength to race. Fails to finish strongly and recovers slowly from racing. Pale gums, rough coat and "picky" eating.

MANAGEMENT: Ensure the highest level of nutrition, in particular adequate levels of iron, Vitamin E and calcium. Check that minimum daily requirements for vitamins, minerals, carbohydrate, protein and fat are supplied by the diet . Consult a Veterinary Surgeon for advice. Worm out greyhound every 4 weeks.

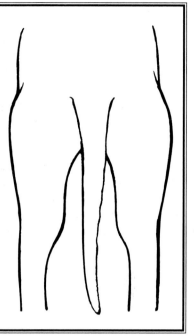

If your dog has a hock injury, broken hocks can be repaired by surgery. Obviously, again the dog would have to be carefully examined by a veterinary surgeon, preferably a specialist in bone surgery, and the hock can be pinned or the bones screwed together to repair them. In this case, although the dog will lose a couple of lengths in form, in many cases the dogs go on to win a number of races quite successfully.

Treatment with magnetic field therapy and a controlled exercise programme help to get mobility back in the joint are very successful. I suggest that you take your dog to a vet who specialises in bone surgery and repair, and ask for his advice. However, in the older dog, there is less chance of a return to full form on the race track.

Q After running my greyhound in an open race, the dog was found to be lame with bruising down the right hind leg. I took the dog to my local vet and after examination he was found to have a lump near the satorious muscle. The vet gave him three sessions of laser treatment over a period of four weeks, and then recommended a hand-slip. **87.**

The dog was OK after this, according to the vet, and so a week later we gave the dog a 500 metre solo, and the following day the dog was found to be very lame with a lot of bruising and swelling on the right side of its hip. The trainer recommended a ten-week lay-off, which she had recommended in the first place. What would you suggest as treatment?

A It appears that the bruising and enlargement of the muscle was due to a racing injury and tearing of the muscle fibres. Generally, a combination of rest and ultrasonic or laser treatment are recommended as the best method to replace bruising and repair torn muscles. The four week period that you gave your dog would be adequate in most cases. However, the dog should be introduced to hand slipping over 150-200 metres two or three times over a period of a

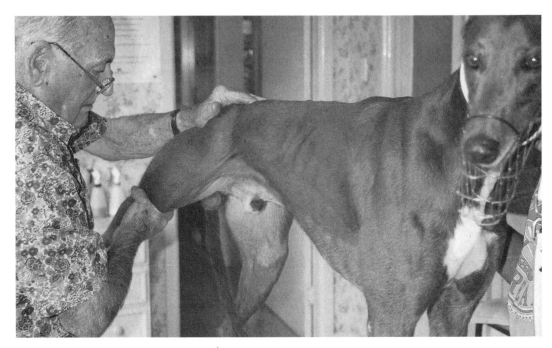

Check for soreness in the upper right leg muscles in a greyhound that runs wide out of corners on the track. Carefully examine (palpate) each muscle, and then extend the leg back to check for resistance or discomfort.

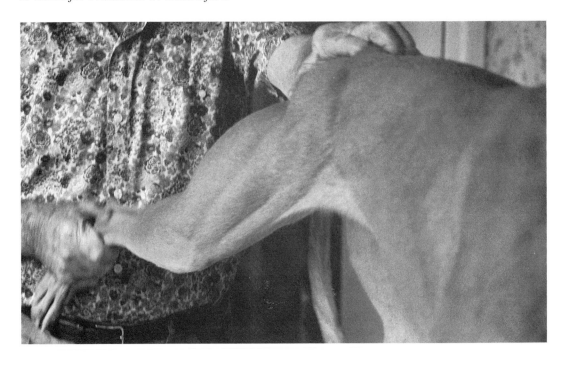

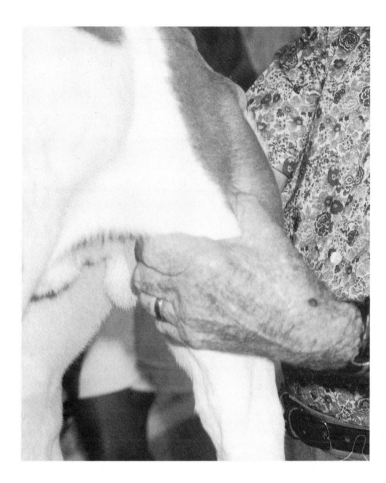

Carefully press on the anchorage points on the midline between the back legs for soreness or tearing of the insertion of the gracilus or "back" muscle in greyhounds that run wide on the corners and fail to gallop hard to the finish.

week or two to tone up and strengthen the muscles following a rest period. It may have been that the dog was reintroduced to racing too early and increased the risk of him tearing another muscle. Alternatively, the second muscle injury may have been present in the initial case, and flared up again once the dog was galloped. In this case, it would be correct to give the dog as long a time as possible for recovery. I am sure that your vet would have given the dog adequate time and treatment of the type and degree of injury he sustained initially. However, in my opinion, you may have introduced your dog back to racing too early, without adequate toning up and strengthening of the muscles following the injury.

During the ten-week lay-off I would suggest you give the dog adequate physiotherapy, including massage of the affected muscles with a product such as MR Iodised Oil. Therapy with magnetopulse or a muscle contractor may also be useful. The dog can then be walked and trotted on the lead each day after about four weeks of rest and physiotherapy. After six weeks the dog can be hand slipped over 100 metres two or three times a week to strengthen the muscles and tone them for galloping. After seven to eight weeks the dog can be hand slipped over 150-200 metres two or three times a week. Ensure the dog undergoes a thorough muscle check by your vet before galloping him in a trial over race distance, or particularly prior to racing.

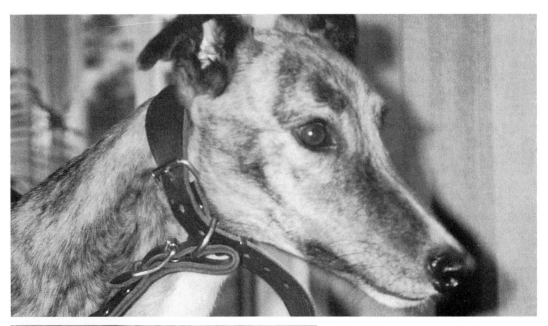

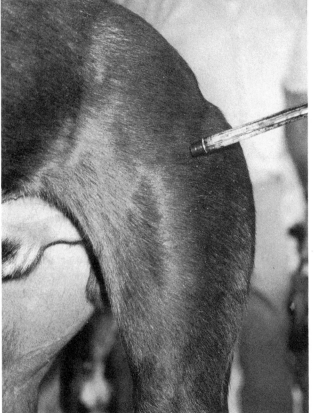

ABOVE: In a greyhound that runs wide when racing, carefully examine the right hind leg, left shoulder, and upper neck muscles for soreness. If the animal is worse under lights, check the eyes for pupil closing reflex by shining a torch in the eye in dim light.

LEFT: The left hip support area is a common spot for soreness, which can result in loss of driving power up the straights of a track and is often associated with soreness and pressure on the lumbo-sacral area. Chronic soreness can result in muscle wastage over the area. This greyhound suffered a race track injury, resulting in swelling of the hip area which the animal favoured even after return to training.

TRACK LEG

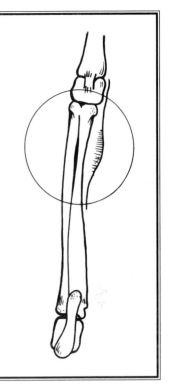

CAUSE: The elbow striking the inside of the hind leg above hock during galloping. Results in bruising and blood vessel rupture under the skin.

TEST: Apply red lipstick to outside of left elbow. Run greyhound around circular track. If hitting, red smear will be present on hock leg area.

FIRST AID: Apply cold packs to area. In mild cases, apply a bandage to the area for 3-4 days. Apply a lubricant such as petroleum jelly to outside elbow and over track leg area.

MANAGEMENT: Severe cases should be referred to a veterinary surgeon for treatment. A complete musculo-skeletal examination of the greyhound should be carried out to determine if underlying injury changes the path of the limbs. A rubber patch stuck on by skin glue will protect badly bruised track leg areas.

Q In the last three months my dog has burst a blood vessel in his back leg three times. I have taken him to the local vet and after the third time he reckons the dog should be put down as there is nothing that can be done for him. I would like to know what you think and if there is a cure or treatment available? **88.**

A From your description, I am not sure where the blood vessel that has burst on a number of occasions is located on your greyhound's leg. If it is in the track leg area, above the hock on the inside, then it usually responds to treatment quite well.

The normal course of treatment for a track leg type injury is to apply an ice pack immediately after the injury occurs, held in place for two or three minutes by an elastic bandage. Repeat two or three times a day to reduce bleeding and swelling. This applies pressure and cold to the area and prevents further bleeding of the broken blood vessel. Then after four to five days the fluid from the blood blister, or haematoma, is withdrawn from the area and a small amount of corticosteroid hormone injected into the area. The area is then bandaged and the dog rested for two to three weeks. This treatment would obviously need to be carried out by your veterinary surgeon.

After seven to ten days, daily applications of an ointment such as Hirudoid or Pergalen ointment can be applied to the area to help healing of the bruised tissue. When the dog recommences training it is best to grease the track leg area and the outside of the elbow on the same side with a petroleum jelly-type ointment.

Because the injury is usually associated with abnormal flight path of the front leg, it is necessary

If a greyhound deviates from its normal free-flowing galloping action, this can result in an injury such as track leg.

to have the dog thoroughly checked out in the shoulder area for an underlying injury that could be causing the dog to turn his elbows out when galloping. If the condition is due to a burst blood vessel in some other part of his leg, I would accept the opinion given by your own veterinary surgeon. If the injury is being caused as a result of striking during galloping, then you will need to have your dog thoroughly examined by your veterinary surgeon for an underlying muscle injury. If the vessel is bleeding under the skin, then the type of treatment as suggested for track leg, would be beneficial in preventing blood leakage and in aiding the healing of the area.

89. Q **I have a four-month-old pup who, whilst off the leash, harmed himself. After X-rays, I am told he has broken his growth plate in his hind leg. What, if any, are the chances of him ever racing?**

A In most cases, the stifle growth plate is the one that is fractured in young pups. However, simply applying a well-fitted cast to the leg to include the joint and the growth plate, providing the growth plate is still well aligned to the bone axis, is usually adequate to allow healing. In many cases in greyhounds, inserting wires or pins to stabilise the growth plate dislodgement is unsuccessful, and often results in arthritis in the joint at a later stage. However, you need to be guided by your own vet's advice on the relative merits of placing the leg in a simple cast and inserting a stabilising pin.

Although young pups may not show much improvement for about three months in a cast, and will still be reluctant to use the leg to walk with after this period, they usually make a rapid recovery and go on to return to racing without any long term effects. Your vet would take X-rays after the cast removal to make sure the growth plate is repositioned and attached, and if this has occurred, then the greyhound has every chance of proceeding and being able to withstand racing.

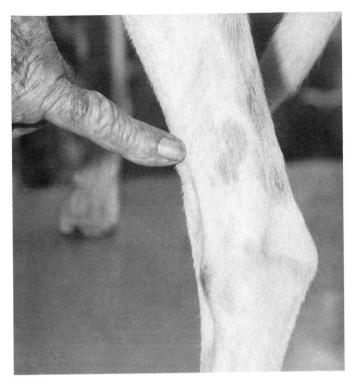

Fracture of the fine fibula bone can occur when greyhounds bump or collide during a race. A greyhound may lose a couple of lengths in speed, and within 7-10 days, a small, hard lump usually develops over the fracture site. It is easily confirmed by feeling the area where the prominent vein passes over the outside front border of the hind limbs, just above the hock. Treatment with pain killers initially to reduce discomfort, and rest for 14-21 days to allow the fracture to heal, is recommended.

CRAMP

Q I own a two-and-a-half-year-old greyhound, which I have reared from the age of five months. I would be grateful if you could give me some information. **90.**

I trialled my dog over a distance of 484m and he seemed OK, but I was told that he was a galloper, and that he was running on and needed a longer distance. After a few trials he pulled up with a tendon, which meant he had to be rested for three months. Two months of that was just resting, and the last month I was slowly building him up from walking to a trial. He was OK after his first trial with no sign of lameness. I then booked him in for another trial and by this time he had had plenty of walking and a few sprints.

When I trialled him I put him over 484m and he broke very well, but as soon as he hit the first bend he seemed to slow up and the other two dogs were well in front. But he still carried on running, although he slowed and stopped stretching out. When I went to the paddock the trainer told me he was lame in his front leg and had cramp. But it was his back leg he was more concerned about.

We now have him home, but it is a shame to leave him because he is such a beautifully-bred dog. Could you answer the following:

a). Could it be his back leg?
b). What is cramp caused by, and could it cause the lameness?
c). How long should I rest him, and what exercise would you suggest?
d). Could the lameness come back again after rest if he raced again?
e). Could you suggest anything for his pads and his muscles?

CRAMPING

(Mild)

CAUSE: The underlying reason for cramping has not been fully determined. Unfit greyhounds are highly prone to cramping in the muscles of the loins and back. Fit greyhounds are unlikely to cramp.
TEST: Press down on back and loin muscles for signs of pain and swelling.

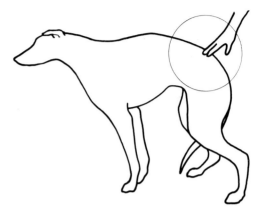

MANAGEMENT: Severe cases – seek Veterinary advice immediately. Do not make the greyhound walk. Mild cases/quick recovery cases; gently massage affected muscle groups. Keep greyhound warm. Ensure the greyhound is not dehydrated and is fit for the distance to race. Consult a Veterinary Surgeon for advice.

A It is difficult to give a diagnosis of his problems without a thorough examination. I would suggest that you take your greyhound to your veterinary surgeon for a thorough examination to find out whether it is a tendon injury in the front leg, or whether he had evidence of cramping up in the hind legs.

From your description, it is most likely to be cramping, particularly as he slowed up and stopped stretching out. It is very uncommon for greyhounds to cramp in their front legs, and most common in the back and hind legs.

However, depending on the severity of his original tendon problem, three months' rest may not be sufficient to completely heal up the injury. It is not uncommon for greyhounds to cramp in one back leg, particularly on the right leg, as they propel themselves around the track. Normally, it appears after the first bend, and from your description it may be localised in the back leg.

The underlying cause of cramping is not known at this time. However, it is definitely associated with body salt imbalances, lack of potassium or calcium in the diet, stress from excitement, and running a dog over too long a distance than he is trained for. It could be that your greyhound has also pulled a muscle in one of his hind legs, which has the same symptoms as cramping, particularly as he continued and finished the race. Again, this condition is determined by a finger examination by your vet.

As regards cramping generally, the dog should be rested for at least five to seven days with light walking, and depending on the degree of cramping, the dog can then be brought back into training and galloped again within two to three weeks. I would suggest that you ensure the dog is on physiological salt replacers such as Betacel, calcium powder such as Calci-D, and vitamin E such as White-E. Also, warm the muscles along the back and hind legs by massage, and trot your dog out on a lead, up and down the kennel area, before a race.

If the dog had a muscle injury, then the lameness is sure to return if he is raced again without an adequate healing period. If it is cramping, provided he is given rest and supplemented with physiological salts, vitamin E and calcium, there is little risk he will cramp again. However, you must ensure the dog is adequately fit for his distance, and is prepared properly by trialling him two or three times over the distance he is to race.

There are various treatments available for pads and muscles. Soft pads can be dried out and hardened with a drying preparation such as Padaid Paint. Hard, dry, cracked pads should be moisturised with a smear of neatsfoot oil twice daily, or a product such as Paidaid cream. Generally, linaments such as Iodised Oil or Radian B linament are available for massage into the muscles over injured and sore spots.

Q **When my pup first began his schooling trials he showed no signs of cramping, but as** **91.** **he got fitter and faster he started to cramp after almost every trial, usually on his way back from the pick up. Sometimes he would lie down and other times he would stand with his head drooped low to the ground. These attacks would last for perhaps five or six minutes, then the dog would appear to be perfectly all right again with no apparent side effects. He receives all the usual additives suggested for cases of cramp (i.e. vitamin E, vitamin C, bonemeal and Betacel) but these do not seem to improve the condition. I have always had a feeling that the problem could be a respiratory one, and that insufficient oxygen was being carried by the blood to the muscles of the back legs.**

I would be grateful for any advice you can give me and whether you consider this to be a possibility, or is there insufficient time during a 280 metre trial for this problem to develop.

A The symptoms you describe are certainly consistent with a cramping problem. Arthritis in the coupling joint in the spine just in front of the rump area can cause a greyhound to wobble in the back legs in the last stages of a race. However, the dog usually shows pain when the back is pressed downwards just in front of the hindquarters.

A cramping problem may also be suspected if your pup passes dark urine for 24 hours after a test trial. If this is the case, I suggest that you take him to your own vet for a thorough check-up, preferably within a couple of hours of a trial where the problem has occurred.

As regards the respiratory problem causing problems with oxygen uptake, then in most cases I would suspect the greyhound would show signs of respiratory distress and gasping for air. However, one should also consider a heart problem, particularly if he dog had contact with pups suffering from parvo-virus disease when it was still a puppy. Your vet would be able to check the dog's heart for you and perhaps take an electro-cardiograph to check for abnormalities. However, any heart trouble usually results in poor performance and cannot be easily rectified.

Q **I have a 17-month-old pup who has just started racing. After his second and fourth** **92.** **races, over 285 and 480 metres respectively, I noticed that when he finished his back legs seemed to wobble and be weak; this lasted for five minutes. He also tried to evacuate his bowels and seemed to be straining.**

I first suspected dehydration and purchased some Betacel, but this doesn't seem to do the trick. I feed him on Wafcol 20 or brown bread with 1 lb mince or horsemeat, cabbage, potatoes, honey, black treacle, eggs, milk, Weetabix, brewer's yeast and 50mg ascorbic acid daily. The only thing I haven't given him is vitamin E in any form.

I walk and gallop him and he looks fit; his eyes are clear, he does not carry excessive weight, but he is not skinny. He sleeps in a warm, well ventilated, hygienic kennel. He has had all his injections and is wormed regularly. Can you help me find the trouble?

MUSCLE SORENESS

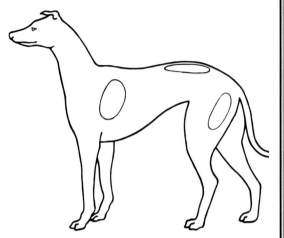

(After racing)

CAUSE: High speed galloping results in a build-up of lactic acid in back, and hind leg muscles. This causes stiffness and soreness after racing, leading to "sour attitude" and loss of appetite. Most common in greyhounds that are not fit for distance, that attempt to catch the field after a check and over exert themselves, or that are dehydrated. Acids leach into the blood resulting in ACIDOSIS.

TEST: The greyhound may have failed to finish strongly. Pressing on the back and hind leg will cause discomfort and pain reaction from major muscles, rather than a specific muscle.

MANAGEMENT: Ensure fresh drinking water is available at all times. Massage back and leg muscles before racing. After trialling or racing, jog greyhound on lead for 5 minutes on arrival at home kennels to improve muscle blood flow and remove acids. When racing, ensure greyhound is fit for distance, and not dehydrated. In severe cases, consult your Veterinary Surgeon.

A There are a number of conditions that could cause this type of problem in your young pup. In young dogs, excessive fatigue during galloping can tire the dog and result in muscle weakness after a race. In these cases, the greyhound becomes uncoordinated and often sits down to rest after a race.

In some cases dogs develop a form of arthritis in the 'coupling joint' where their spinal column meets their pelvic bone structure. This causes pain after exercise and the dog may wobble at the end of a race and fail to finish strongly. Again, this lasts for a short time and the dogs usually recover by the time they have walked back to the kennelling house. If you suspect this type of injury, I would suggest you take your dog to your own vet for a thorough examination.

In other cases, dogs may suffer from a mild form of cramping, which can cause them to step short and exhibit wobbles in their back legs. This normally wears off too, by the time the dog gets back to the kennelling area. In this case examine the dog's muscles along his back and down the back legs as soon as he is caught in the pick-up area after a race.

If the dog reacts to pain or shows stiffness and hardness in the muscles, I would suggest you put him on 200iu of vitamin E, e.g. White-E, 1 tsp of electrolytes, e.g. Betacel, and 3 tsp of calcium powder, e.g. DCP-340 or Calci-D. If this form of mild cramping has been causing the problem, this treatment should help him to reduce the problem within 10-14 days.

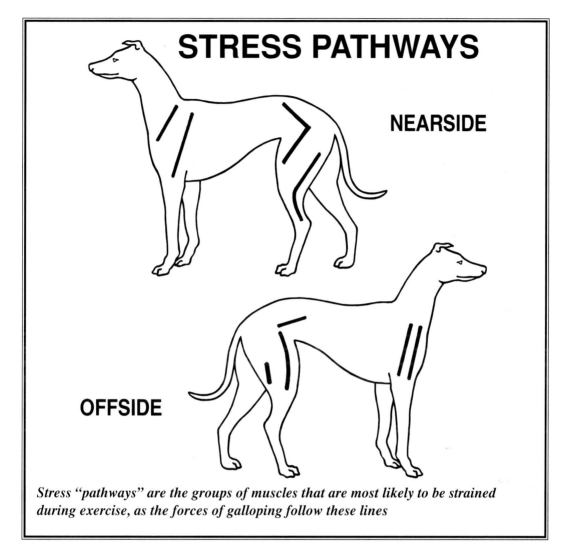

STRESS PATHWAYS

NEARSIDE

OFFSIDE

Stress "pathways" are the groups of muscles that are most likely to be strained during exercise, as the forces of galloping follow these lines

You certainly seem to be feeding your dog an adequate diet. However, you may need to increase the amount of mince to 1 1/4lb to ensure the dog gets adequate meat, and two slices of brown bread, depending on how many potatoes you feed. Do not feed any more than 1-2 eggs per day as this can cause a deficiency of the biotin vitamin, and may result in dry, flakey skin, brittle toenails or loss of performance.

Q I would greatly appreciate your opinion and advice on my greyhound's performance. **93.** He is a 20-month-old puppy which I reared along with his litter sister from five weeks of age to schooling age of 13 months. They had a good rearing with plenty of freedom and a good diet. Friends offered to school them; they took them on at 13 months and schooled them well and did not rush them in any way. They duly raced over 515 yards. The dog won both his starts (all ages) and was very impressive. The bitch performed creditably

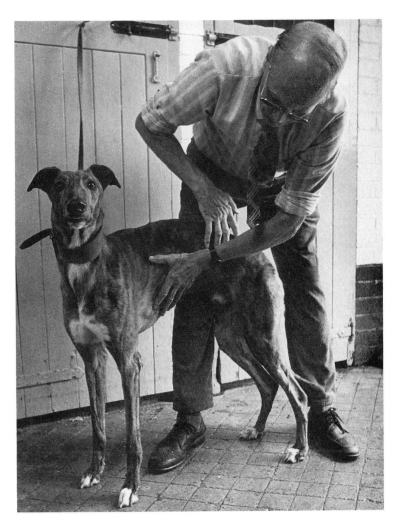

Massaging a greyhound, as demonstrated by top trainer Geroge Curtis, is a useful method of relieving muscle soreness, particularly when a good quality linament is used.

and was a close up second in both her starts, also all ages. Then we had problems. The dog damaged a nail in his second race and the bitch developed kennel sickness. So I took them home for about ten weeks. Owing to the inclemency of the weather they did not trial until the end of February and early March. The dog had three trials in daylight and one under lights, all over 515 metres. He showed good early pace and was put on the race card.

He trapped fairly well in his race and went into the lead at the first bend. He had increased his lead to at least 4 lengths on the back straight, moving freely and well. By the top straight the pursuing dog began to close and then drew level with my dog, matching him stride for stride and then drew clear. At this stage it was clear my dog was pulling up, and he did so abruptly, losing all interest in the race and made no further effort to chase. Apparently he did not show any signs of injury or cramp. He appeared to be propping himself as if he were trying to avoid running into something.

He is an alert, energetic, muscular type of dog and gives the impression of being keen and intelligent, and is superbly bred for track racing. He raced at 72lb (32.7 kg) which his trainer said was a little overweight. He otherwise appears to be in very good health.

I am also concerned about his litter sister who has a peculiar problem following a trial or race. It shows up as a noticeable bounding pulsation towards the end of her rib cage on the left side. It is obvious to the eye and on palpation feels very full and bounding and lasts about 15-20 minutes following a run. She is not unduly distressed with it at the time, but seems a bit tired afterwards. I first noticed it following a trial. I was unhappy about it; it seemed so forceful and I asked her handlers if they could have her examined by a a vet, which they did. He said that there was not anything the matter with her and that, in fact, she had a very strong athletic heart.

A From your description it appears that your dog may have developed a very mild type of cramping during the race which, in many cases, is not obvious once the dog recovers after racing. In this case, it is best to examine the dog immediately the dog finishes the race for

TRAINER'S TIP

In a greyhound that slows down in the last half of a race, catch it immediately after the race, and check its back and left hind leg muscles for "knotting" and hardness associated with low-grade cramping. Once the greyhound is caught and walked back to the kennel area, the symptoms of cramping may disappear, and the poor performance put down to some other reason. In affected greyhounds, supplements of calcium, Vitamin E and physiological electrolytes are often useful in preventing further cramping episodes of this type.

signs of muscle hardness over the rump and down the back legs. In many cases, by the time the dog walks 20-30 yards, or is caught following a race, clinical signs of cramping have disappeared.

The dog could also have developed a muscle injury. The change to a 'stilted' gait may indicate a shoulder or front leg injury, or even 'shin soreness' in a young greyhound racing on a circle track. In this case, I would suggest you have the dog thoroughly examined by your veterinary surgeon.

If the problem can be attributed to cramping, I would suggest that you add an electrolyte replacer to his diet. Also ensure the greyhound is given adequate calcium in his diet (2 tsp per day). Always warm him up by massaging the back and hind leg muscles briskly before galloping or racing. Supplements of vitamin E, such as in White-E, are also often used to help prevent cramping in greyhounds.

As regards his litter sister with the peculiar bounding heart pulsation, it is probably quite a normal condition. The movement of the heart, called the cardiac impulse, is often transmitted to the chest wall. This is more noticeable in lean athletic animals such as greyhounds, and it is quite a normal event. The degree of cardiac impulse that is noticeable on the chest wall is dependent on the size of the heart, the force of the heartbeat and the contact between the heart and the inside chest wall.

In a greyhound that has just completed a gallop, particularly if she has a large heart, it is often quite noticeable. In some animals an enlarged heart may signify heart disease. However, if she is not unduly distressed after galloping, then this is unlikely to be an underlying problem. If you are concerned, have your bitch examined by your veterinary surgeon.

94. Q **I wonder if you could give me some advice on a problem I am having with one of our dogs. About nine months ago, the dog completed a race and arrived back at the paddock, apparently suffering from severe cramp in the lower back. He walked with very stiff rear legs, and any attempt to lie down brought severe pain. He stayed in this condition for about ten days, and then improved. I rested him for two more weeks, and then he ran and won races.**

Three months later, the day after a race, the same symptoms occurred and now within the last week he has done it again. The pain seems to be in the lower back, and the dog cannot be touched in this region without distress. At first I thought it was just this one dog. However, recently one of my bitches did exactly the same, showing the same symptoms.

People at the track say the dog has cramped up. If this is so, does recovery normally take this long, or is it something more serious? Is there any way to prevent this cramping?

I do not walk the dogs, but they are galloped in fields near home twice a week. As the dog has done this three times, should I consider retiring him? He is three and a half years old, and I consider him my best dog – he has won two of the track championships.

A From your description it appears that your dog suffers from a severe case of cramping. This condition is called rhabdomyolysis. Usually, affected dogs dehydrate badly and lose quite a lot of bodyweight. They urinate dark-coloured urine and go off their feed for a number of days. In severe cases it may be fatal.

If the condition has occurred once, the affected dog is more prone to developing the condition when galloped again. However, from your description the condition could also be due to a lumbosacral disc problem, which is common in some greyhounds. Normally these greyhounds wobble from side to side when coming out of the traps, and usually pull up with soreness and pain in the back just in front of their pelvic area.

I would suggest that you take your dog along to your own vet for a thorough examination. Your vet will decide whether it is a spinal problem or a muscular problem. However, it seems odd that one of your bitches has developed the same symptoms. I would suggest that you ensure that you exercise your dogs more regularly, without excessive walking. If the dogs are locked up for two or three days at a time without exercise, obviously this may increase the risk of cramping and other muscular conditions when they are allowed to gallop.

I would suggest that you take your dogs out for a walk for about 3/4 of a mile a day and make sure that your dogs are well warmed up before galloping. This can be done by massaging the muscles of the back and back legs, and walking the dog briskly around for five minutes before allowing the dog to gallop at full speed. This should reduce the risk of cramping.

Q **My two-and-a half year-old bitch occasionally cramps when getting up after lying down for any length of time. So far it has occurred five times in the past four weeks – three times in the right tricep muscle (on different occasions), and twice (during one evening) in her right seminembranosis (inside) muscle. She is unable to put the affected legs to the ground and cries out if any attempt is made to touch or massage the muscle, which is absolutely solid during these attacks, which can last for a couple of minutes.** **95.**

My bitch appears sound and does not cramp during or after racing or exercise gallops. She is given all the suggested anti-cramp additives (e.g. Betacel, vitamin E, vitamin C, calcium) and she looks a picture of health. At the moment of writing, she is in her third week of her yearly season. Please can you offer any advice on this type of cramping?

A It is very uncommon for a greyhound to suffer the same type of cramps as those commonly called 'night cramps' suffered by humans. From your description it appears that the cramps are occurring in different muscles on different occasions, and not isolated to any one muscle. In humans, the common theory for isolated muscle cramping is that it is due to reduced blood flow patterns, pressure on nerve supply to individual muscles, body salt abnormalities, and possibly even an hereditary condition. It is also interesting to note that your bitch does not cramp during gallops. The anti-cramp additives such as Betacel, vitamin E and calcium are useful to help prevent cramping during a race. I doubt if there is a relationship between her 'season' and the cramping.

As far as treatment is concerned, I would suggest you consult your vet regarding supplementation with a tablet containing the mineral selenium. Selenium is associated with cramping in some animals, and may be useful to help prevent cramping in your bitch. In human cramps the drug quinine was traditionally used to prevent night cramping. If the affected leg appears to be colder than the other legs during the cramping episode, then a drug to correct the blood flow may be of benefit. Your vet would be able to advise you on the best treatment to use to overcome this condition.

Some authorities claim that doses of vitamin B15 are useful in helping to improve blood flow to muscles. It would also be of interest to check up on her family ancestry to determine whether there is an incidence of cramping in her bloodline. I would suggest that you take your greyhound to your own vet for a thorough examination immediately after the cramping episode.

Q **I have a bitch who, after racing or strenuous exercise, passes urine with a high alkaline content. At all other times her urine is slightly acid (which I believe is correct). My bitch is occasionally muscle sore, especially if she runs an extra circuit** **96.**

after her race. This soreness can occur more than 48 hours later. I have read that dogs with alkaline urine after a race might be more prone to cramping (this seems to be the case with my bitch), and one solution would be to acidify the urine with sodium acid phosphate and Methionine.

Contrary to this, I have also read that to help prevent some forms of cramp (i.e. acidosis) it is useful to give Neutradex before and after a race, to buffer the acids produced by extreme muscle activity. Neutradex contains sodium citrate, which has the effect of making urine more alkaline. The two suggestions seem to contradict each other. Please can you explain why? Which would you advise me to use?

A The exact process that may be occurring in your bitch is somewhat difficult and confusing to explain. The acid content of the urine in greyhounds is dependent on the diet, degree of dehydration, presence of bladder infections, and time of racing.

Greyhounds on a meat-based diet usually excrete an acid urine and as the dry food content is increased, the urine normally turns alkaline. Excitable or nervy greyhounds, particularly those who have developed a chronic form of dehydration from excessive, excited panting or barking, commonly have a more alkaline urine. This is due to the enforced loss of carbon dioxide gas from the lungs and the accumulation of acid electrolytes in the blood which have a 'positive' charge, which is compensated for and balanced by the excretion of bicarbonate (alkaline) salt with a 'negative' charge in the urine.

Bitches, in particular, are more prone to low grade bladder infections, which usually result in the breakdown of protein in the urine to give an alkaline urine. These bitches have a habit of squatting frequently to pass small amounts of urine to help relieve the irritation in the bladder. And lastly, fast muscular activity results in the formation of lactic acid in the muscles. This lactic acid is metabolised in the liver and heart to energy, and the 'overflow' is excreted for up to 12-24 hours in the urine. However, in bitches with a low grade bladder infection, it is thought that these acids are metabolised by germs and excreted as increased alkaline after a race. In most greyhounds, a combination of all these factors can result in excretion of urine with an acid or alkaline reaction which sometimes has no reflection on the acid-alkaline level of the blood.

As regards her tendency to develop muscle soreness after a race, then this could be due to an accumulation of excess acids in the muscles, which are not released or 'pumped out' from the muscles into the blood quickly enough. In unfit greyhounds or in greyhounds that 'get away' and run an extra lap after a race, it is important to 'trot' them out on a lead immediately they are caught after galloping. About three minutes exercise, at the human 'jogging' pace, helps to 'pump' these acids out of the muscles and prevents stiffness and soreness developing in the 12-48 hour period after a longer gallop.

It is unwise to give products such as Neutradex to greyhounds that have a normally alkaline urine, particularly to bitches suffering from low grade 'cystitis' or bladder infections. Increasing the alkaline content of the urine only serves to encourage the infection to persist. However, in greyhounds that develop signs of muscle soreness, without actually 'cramping' in a race, then Neutradex could be very helpful in increasing the buffering activity in the blood. Neutradex is also used to 'flush' the kidneys after racing and helps to correct dehydration.

In the case of your bitch, I would suggest that you give her a course of 3 Methionine tablets (e.g. Methnine 90), one in the morning, two at night, for five to seven days leading up to a race and test her urine again after racing. However, to help prevent low grade 'cramping' ensure she is on an electrolyte salt mix, such as Betacel, and adequate levels of calcium, such as 2 tsp of dicalcium phosphate powder or Calci-D in her ration. If the condition persists and you consider that her performance is being hampered by an acid-alkaline imbalance, then have your vet carry out some more detailed blood and urine tests.

MISCELLANEOUS

Q My six-year-old retired greyhound bitch has been diagnosed as having suffered a **97.** spinal haemorrhage. I am convinced that the collapse was caused by the anti-inflammatory tablets, but my vet assures me this is not so; he has given them to her before with no ill-effect. Is it possible that she could suffer a severe allergic reaction the second time but not the first?

The reason she was given the anti-inflammatory tablets was continuing lameness of the front left leg, with a very sore pad, which is hard and swollen. The vet X-rayed the foot and the leg, and he says the X-ray shows slight osteoarthritis in the elbow, which is causing her to put her foot down unnaturally, leading to the pad discomfort. He says it is progressive and the only treatment is anti-inflammatory tablets!

Naturally, I have a strong disinclination to administer this treatment but I don't want my dog to suffer. What do you suggest? Her general condition is improving slowly. She enjoys her food and is eager for walks, but she does not walk far before she begins to panic and her lameness worries her. When she stands still she carries her left leg.

A Although you do not mention the type of anti-inflammatory tablets given, certain compounds do increase the risk of bleeding. For example, common aspirin, at higher dose rates, will delay clotting of blood, and where injury has occurred may increase the risk of haemorrhage. Phenylbutazone can have similar effects.

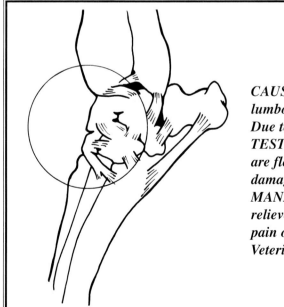

ARTHRITIS

CAUSE: Arthritis can develop in wrists, lumbo-sacral joint, hock and other joints. Due to wear and tear, falls, sprains, fractures.
TEST: Greyhound exhibits pain when joints are flexed. X-rays will indicate extent of bone damage.
MANAGEMENT: Pain and soreness may be relieved by massage. Continued severe joint pain or lameness should be examined by a Veterinary Surgeon.

Theoretically, your bitch may have had severe bruising of the spinal column for some other reason, and when given anti-inflammatory compounds the bruise could have developed into haemorrhage which eventually pressed on the spinal cord. Alternatively, the pain killers may have made her more comfortable and she may have over-stressed an already weakened spinal column, resulting in collapse and spinal paralysis. Old bitches may also develop a form of weak bone structure or osteoporosis, which is caused by loss of calcium from bones on diets that have inadequate calcium.

As regards the recent findings of osteoarthritis in the elbow on X-ray, this could certainly be causing her to jar the pads when exercising. Certainly, anti-inflammatory and pain-killing tablets are usually the most convenient from of treatment.

98. Q **I have a retired racing greyhound bitch, aged six years. I have had her for two years. A fortnight ago she went slightly lame on her left front leg. I took her to the vet and he said it was a toe causing the pain. He gave her an injection and a course of anti-inflammatory tablets.**

The following day I gave her a lead walk at 7 a.m. followed by breakfast with two tablets. Then she went to her bed. At 8.15 a.m. I heard her screaming. She was lying on her side foaming at the mouth. I got her to the vet's and he gave her oxygen. He took an ECG and said her heart was very weak. Her body was hot, but her blood temperature was below normal. He had no idea what was causing it.

She remained in a critical state all the following day. He sent blood samples and took two spine X-rays. The blood test results phoned through proved nothing. There was nothing on the X-rays. He discussed the case with someone at the Liverpool Veterinary College, who suggested it was a spinal haemorrhage, something which usually kills within 24 hours, but if it doesn't there is a good chance of recovery.

Because my vet has not dealt with a case of this kind before, he cannot be specific on any answers to my question. Can you tell me anything about this condition? Is it likely to occur again?

I love this dog, but I really don't think she should suffer a similar attack again. She is now home and seems reasonably happy, although she can only stagger and that with difficulty. I should say I am completely satisfied with the efforts made by the vet. He did his best under the circumstances.

A Although spinal injuries and haemorrhage into the spinal cord could cause the clinical condition that you describe, it is more likely that the bitch has suffered from some sort of reaction to the tablets, or a bite of a poisonous insect. In older greyhounds a mild heart attack may also cause similar symptoms, but if this was the case, it would have shown up if blood enzyme levels were tested within the following 12-24 hours.

It is possible that she had some sort of severe allergic reaction to the anti-inflammatory tablets, particularly if you gave them for the first time after her breakfast. It certainly would be very uncommon for this type of reaction, but not impossible. However, your vet certainly has done everything to try to find out the underlying cause, and also has given the correct treatment.

As regards nursing her, you should be guided by her clinical condition and also response and improvement. Keep her as comfortable as possible, and as she improves allow her to go out in the warm part of the day for a walk. Also pay attention to her diet to ensure she has an adequate, appetising and soft diet that would allow the digestive system to recover and avoid complications such as constipation. Obviously, if a spinal haemorrhage is the underlying cause, then she should be kept as quiet as possible to ensure that the haemorrhage does not recur with exercise or excitement. However, as she is middle-aged she is unlikely to have the energy and 'carefree' attitude of a younger bitch. Let's hope that she recovers fully to live her normal lifespan.

Q I would be grateful if you could provide me with the solution to this mysterious **99.** disease.

CASE HISTORY: Two-year-old black dog, bred in Eire; purchased at twelve weeks and reared on a free range system in Somerset. The dog is 'big boned', and so was allowed to grow on and not raced early. He is fully vaccinated, regularly wormed, and has no known problems. He is a bit of a 'thoroughbred type', and has to be kept well-fed. Ran trials well.
September 21: Sent to racing kennels.
September 29: First trial excellent; no problem in new kennels.
October 14: First symptoms – off food, rapid loss of weight in 24 hours, no temperature, no indication of dog or rat bite etc., nor any external sign of damage to skin.
October 15: Right hock very swollen – given Penbritin injection and tablets.
October 16: Appeared very ill, other hock swollen; still no temperature; off food.
October 17: Further loss of weight; both wrists now swollen and hocks and thigh 'breaking out' in serious blood blotches; further injection of Penbritin given.
October 18: All wrists and hocks 'weeping', but swellings going down.
October 20: Eating again – total weight loss 7 lb.
October 23: Seems himself again; eating four small meals a day; sores still open.
October 28: Returned home to Somerset from kennels.
Present condition: Normal appetite (5 lb lighter); most sores dried up; old self again! No temperature rise or fall throughout illness; dog is now walking out (coated night and day). What I would like to know is:
a). When is it safe to let him off in a paddock?
b). Is it OK to give his annual injection booster, as it is now due?
c). What do you think was the cause, and do you think it could occur in other dogs?
d). Will there be any long term effect on this dog?
 The only other cases known to be similar occurred in a group of twelve dogs in the same kennels in 1972! Nobody I have spoken to can offer a logical solution to the cause of this disease.

A The symptoms you describe appear to be associated with a disease that affects the joints in young greyhounds. There have been a couple of published reports on various types of polyarthritis or joint disease in young greyhounds. It appears that some greyhounds respond to treatment with antibiotics as your greyhound, and others do not respond to any type of treatment.

Although the reason for this type of disease is not known, it is suspected that an infectious agent initiates the disease, which is then carried on by the dog's own immune system to cause severe damage in joints. This could be the case in your greyhound since he has no record of having a temperature or any other problem. However, since one joint was affected initially, and then other joints became affected within three to four days, it appears that the problem was due to a swelling of the tissues around the joint rather than inside the joint.

In most cases, if the internal structures of the joint are involved, the greyhound remains severely lame and does not recover. However, your dog responded to injections of antibiotic, although the other joints became affected during the initial stage of this treatment until the antibiotic started to effectively control the spread of the germ in the blood. It appears that it seems to be similar to an antibiotic responsive to acute swelling around joints that was described some years ago in young greyhounds. It appears that the treatment, which was initiated early in the course of the disease, was effective.

It is important to make sure that the dog is properly looked after and nursed during the recovery phase. If the dog is not lame, then I would suggest it would be safe to let him out into a small paddock for free exercise. I would suggest that you let him out by himself initially so that he does not try to run and compete with other dogs. Once he has strengthened up and regained some of his weight, then you may wish to let him run free with other greyhounds. From your description, the dog has put on about 7lb bodyweight in the two to three weeks since the peak of the disease. You may wish to put the dog on to supplements of vitamin A and vitamin C, as contained in tablets such as Rebound, during the convalescent period, to help reduce stress and aid his recovery.

As regards giving him his regular annual booster, in my opinion you should wait until the dog recovers for another two to three weeks before challenging his immune system with a booster injection. However, if the dog appears to be clinically fit and healthy, then a booster injection would be safe.

It is unlikely that the disease will occur in other dogs in your kennel once the peak of the disease has been reached and the treatment has been effective. However, I would suggest that you take normal quarantine measures by isolating this particular dog for some time until he makes a full recovery. This is particularly important if his sores are still weeping.

As this dog has recovered quite quickly and responded to treatment, it is unlikely there will be any long term effect on the dog. This would be so if the infection only involved the outer structures of the joint. However, if the dog remains lame or internal joint damage occurred, then it is likely the dog will be crippled for racing. You should be able to assess long term prospects in the next month or so as the dog recovers and is able to exercise freely by himself. Since the symptoms occurred in the same kennels about fifteen years ago, it appears that the disease is due to some type of local infectious or other agent.

TREATMENTS

100. Q We suddenly seem to be bombarded by new veterinary technology, and as a greyhound handler I would like to know more about them. I hear other trainers talking about laser therapy, ultrasound, magnetic therapy, etc. though I am convinced that they know less than me but are afraid to admit it.

I realise that the subject is too huge to answer in any great depth, but in basic terms, which treatments suit which injuries and why?

A There are various forms of mechanical and electronic therapy for specific types of injuries in greyhounds. Many of the companies that manufacture the therapy units have brochures and information booklets that outline the types of conditions that their machines can treat. However, many claims are made that overlap between the machines, as every manufacturer lists every conceivable type of injury that responds to specific therapy.

As regards ultrasound treatment, in my opinion, this is still one of the more specific treatments for localised muscle injuries in the racing greyhound. Ultrasound therapy can be targeted at a specific area on the shoulder and hind leg muscles, and the sound waves simply 'massage' the muscle to improve the blood supply and general healing.

Ultrasound therapy cannot be used in severe tears for at least two to five days after the initial injury. Icepacks and cold therapy should be used for at least the first 48 hours to reduce swelling and inflammation, and minimise bleeding in the area. Treatment to minor injuries using ultrasound can be commenced after the ice therapy, and in more serious injuries ultrasound therapy can be commenced within five to seven days.

As regards laser therapy, there have been many claims and counter-claims on the benefits of lasers in treating injuries in greyhounds. However, in my opinion laser therapy appears to be useful in treating specific injuries on bony areas, particularly over the toes, or where tendons attach behind the wrist and ligaments around the knee and hock joints. Generally, I have found it

TRAINER'S TIP

Magnetic Field Therapy (MFT) is considered to aid healing of muscle and bone injuries, possibly by promoting blood circulation and relaxing spasms in injured muscles. The cage unit models, such as the Portamag 500 (illustrated above) are convenient and time saving, as greyhounds can be give MFT for multiple injuries in a relaxed, comfortable cage. This type of MFT machine can be used to warm up muscles prior to racing, and to relax greyhounds after a hard race.

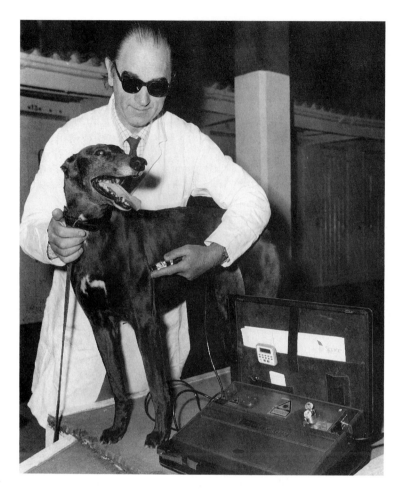

Laser therapy is useful in treating superficial injuries over bony areas, such as on the lower limb below the wrist and hock.

less useful on the deeper muscle injuries in racing greyhounds. Therefore, laser therapy seems to be better on superficial injuries over bony areas such as on the lower limb below the wrist and the hock. There have been many claims for the use of magnetic field therapy in racing greyhounds. Again, various types of machines have been developed, and although magnetic field therapy has been shown to be useful in healing up bone fractures in animals, much of the information on magnetic field therapy is based on practical field experience. In my opinion, magnetic field therapy is very useful for treating general muscle soreness, particularly over the back, shoulder and hind leg muscles. There are both continuous and pulsed magnetic field therapy machines available, including a variation with 'bi-phasic' type operation. The newer machines certainly appear to have more features than the earlier machines. Low power settings can be used to cool and restrict blood flow in legs following injury, and higher settings can be used to increase blood flow and aid healing.

Some machines are equipped with full blankets that can be used to treat a number of muscle injuries at the one time, particularly on the body area, and also warm up a dog for racing. Unfortunately, it is claimed by many trainers that magnetic field therapy tends to dehydrate greyhounds, but if care is taken with the therapy, there seems no adverse effect.

Q We have a Niagara Cyclopad with cycloid polymodulation and massage control. This **101.** is in the form of a flat pad. Although purchased for my own use, do you think it would be of any use to my greyhounds? If so, could you advise us of the best way to obtain greatest benefit i.e. how long to use it, and how often?

A Generally, human machines can be used on greyhounds, but the length of treatment needs to be reduced accordingly. Two to five minutes of treatment twice a day would probably be quite adequate. However, I would recommend that you consult a specialist greyhound physiotherapist as to the best way to use the machine on racing greyhounds. I am sure your own vet would be able to give you full advice on the use of the machine on a greyhound with a particular injury.

Q I have recently heard a lot of talk about the use of acupuncture in treating certain **102.** injuries. Does the veterinary profession recognise this treatment? If so, can you tell me which injuries it can help?

A Recently, many trainers and physiotherapists have been claiming benefit of acupuncture in prevention and treatment of greyhound cramp, but there seems little evidence to support this in the long term. Although some dogs seem to improve, many dogs still continue to cramp, even after a course of treatment. However, this may rely on the skill of inserting the acupuncture needles or laser therapy on acupuncture points, rather than the benefit of acupuncture generally.

Acupuncture is probably better accepted by the greyhound specialist in the veterinary profession than in any other field of medicine. Whilst the benefits of acupuncture are recognised in many human sports injuries, there is little direct evidence to suggest that acupuncture has many definite benefit in specific greyhound injuries. Some veterinarians believe it is more suited to soft tissue injuries than muscle and bone injuries. Other veterinarians have had good success with it in treating joint and bone injuries, rather than muscle and soft tissue injuries.

In many cases, the acupuncture technique is also complemented by other forms of therapy, such as injecting mixtures of B12, antibiotics and local anaesthetics into the area after the acupuncture treatment has been carried out. Although acupuncture therapy appears to be beneficial for acute muscle injuries, many trainers become disenchanted with the length and expense of the treatment time required.

An Australian veterinarian, Dr Gilchrist, has published a book on the use of acupuncture for small animals, including acupuncture points and treatment of various injuries in racing greyhounds. There are specific 'formulae' for administering acupuncture to specific points for individual conditions, but some experience is required to get the best overall results in the long term. Sprung toes, sore shins and a variety of other conditions seem to respond to either needle or laser acupuncture, although many of these conditions also improve with other forms of therapy combined with adequate rest periods.

I would suggest you contact your local greyhound veterinarian for referral to a greyhound physiotherapy unit which specialises in acupuncture for greyhounds.

Chapter Four

RESPIRATORY DISEASES

103. **Q** I would like some advice on two of my greyhounds. One is a dog who is three years old. I would like to know why he coughs up phlegm about one hour after he has been racing. The phlegm is very clear and like the white of an egg. He swallows it straight away and does not do it again until he races again. The strange thing is he only does it three times.

My bitch is three years old, and in the last two months, after racing she comes off the track, feeling wet and cold as if sweating.

A The symptoms you describe could be caused by infection with the 'windpipe worm' that lives in the lower airways. The incidence of infection with this worm is increasing and any greyhound with a chronic cough should have the lower airways checked by a flexible 'scope' by your vet. Treatment with a worming compound, of a dose recommended by your vet, is the only form of treatment. The phlegm coughed up can also be checked for worm eggs by your vet.

If the greyhound does not appear to be distressed with symptoms of respiratory problems, it could be related to collection of saliva in the throat area. Some dogs suffer from a low grade irritation to the tonsil area which is aggravated by intake of cold air during galloping. It is often referred to as a 'biley throat' and may be aggravated by dusty bedding or track surfaces.

If the dog appears distressed after racing, then I suggest that you have him examined by your own veterinary surgeon. This is because low grade airway disease may be present from a previous bout of kennel cough or other respiratory disease. This may not only hamper his performance, but can lead to long term irritation and damage in the windpipe and lower lung area. It may be beneficial for you to give him a trial and then take him to your vet within the hour to have his throat examined and at about the time he normally coughs.

In older greyhounds with heart damage, fluid will sometimes build up in the lungs, particularly overnight. In some cases the greyhounds appear to try to cough it up when being taken for exercise in the morning. However, it does not commonly occur in younger greyhounds.

If low grade irritation to the back of the throat is suspected, then administration of 1-2 tsp of glycerine over the back of the tongue about twenty minutes before galloping sometimes helps to lubricate a dry throat and reduce the risk of coughing after exercise. A 'biley throat' may be cleared by giving a dose of Bilex or 1 tsp of Agarol 3 days before racing.

As regards your bitch that has a cold back, I would suspect that it could be due to low grade build-up of acids in the muscles after exercise. Alternatively, it could be due to a circulation

Respiratory problems will come to light after the stress of competing in a trial or a race.

problem when insufficient blood is getting to these muscles after exercise, particularly if they are slightly 'blown up' due to accumulation of fluid in the muscle areas due to low grade acidosis.

If she has no history of being sore over the back area, or even cramping, and she has had otherwise good performance, then it is no cause for concern. In fact, some greyhounds appear cold over the back area after a gallop, even though they feel warm over the hind leg muscles. However, if you are particularly worried about it, then I suggest that you have your bitch examined thoroughly by your own veterinary surgeon.

104.

Q **I bought a dog and he was suffering from a cough, and he weighed 57 lb instead of 62 lb when he was racing fit. My local vet prescribed antibiotic tablets that cleared the cough, and the dog was also wormed.**

Since then I have given the dog Cytacon 1312, but he is only 58 lb and off his food. I have tried to clean him out with common soda wrapped in cheese, as he will not let you open his jaws – if you try, he has a bite at your hand. When he cleans himself out his stools start OK, but are very watery, yellowish and frothy as if full of phlegm.

Although his cough has gone, I think he still has phlegm in his throat. He has had five trials on five different tracks and qualified on all of them. If he is put right, he will be a good dog. I hope you can help.

A The symptoms you describe could be related to a number of problems. In greyhounds that are raced whilst suffering from a cold or kennel cough, internal damage to the lungs may result. However, dogs with lung problems usually become distressed when galloped, and this does not appear to be a problem in your dog, as he has qualified in his trials. A thorough examination by your vet, and even an X-ray of the chest may be worthwhile if you suspect a lung problem. Your vet will also check for signs of the 'windpipe worm' that lives in the lower airways. These worms cause chronic coughing and affect overall performance.

However, the build-up of phlegm is often associated with tonsillitis or throat irritation. His habit of resisting medication and his poor appetite could indicate a tonsillitis or throat problem. Again, a thorough examination by your vet is recommended.

The colour and consistency of his stools could indicate a liver or pancreas problem. Chronic liver damage may have developed before you purchased the dog. Dogs with liver problems often lose weight, have a poor appetite and fail to perform. Their stools may be yellowish in colour, 'fatty' in appearance and coated with mucus. A course of B complex vitamins and 2-3 Methnine 90 tablets daily for a week or so may help the liver recover. However, a physical check and blood test by your vet must be considered if the dog does not improve.

For greyhounds with a 'frothy' throat, many trainers use a laxative agent, such as 2 tsp of Agarol, or tsp of Altan powder on the night feed once a week for a couple of weeks, with reported good results. I suggest that since the problem appears to be hampering his general health and performance, then a thorough examination by your vet would certainly be worthwhile.

105. Q **My dog has a breathing problem which is only apparent when he pulls up after racing. If a very slight (and I emphasise 'very slight') pressure is applied with the fingertips to the lower part of the windpipe, it noticeably restricts his breathing and a wheezy vibration can be heard and felt. If the fingers are moved higher up the throat the 'something' gets much less. Sometimes at the pick-up I have heard when I can only describe as a whistling sound as he breathes.**

I have taken him to two vets. One suggested that he might have a lung worm or a worm cyst in his throat. The other, after giving my dog a general anaesthetic and an exploratory probe, said that his problem could possibly be caused by a mis-shapen epiglottis, and as far as he could tell, the rest of the trachea looked alright.

My reaction to this, as a layman, is that the wheezing sound originates much too low down in the windpipe to be caused by the epiglottis, and it is only when the throat is touched that the effect is heard and felt. Friends at the track where I race, have suggested he may have sand or other foreign substances down his throat and that I should vomit him. I have not done this so far, and I would like your views on this before I attempt it.

My dog is 16 months old, and at the moment I am trialling him over sprint distances of not more than 300 yards. Although he looks likely to make the grade, I would like to know how much this breathing problem is likely to limit his potential. More important, with the limited amount of information I have been able to supply, what do you think is the likely cause?

A I appreciate you supplying as much information on your dog's problem as possible. However, it is still difficult to give specific advice on what could be the underlying cause of the problem.

You mention that it appears that his breathing is restricted when the lower part of his windpipe is pressed very lightly. If this happens only after exercise, it could be due to the collapse of the windpipe where it enters the chest cavity and could restrict the airway. If the problem occurs even when the dog is at rest, then there may be some type of other obstruction to the windpipe. For instance, a flap of lining from the windpipe may be obstructing the airway.

It may be necessary to take your dog to have a full examination with a bronchoscope into his lower airways and lung passages. Unfortunately, if it is a problem that occurs only after the dog has galloped, it may be difficult to examine the exact underlying cause if the dog cannot be examined immediately after exercise. In some cases X-rays may be useful in determining any abnormal constriction of the windpipe as it enters the chest. But in many dogs that appear to be normal, there will appear to be some flattening of the windpipe in this area. If the dog had a foreign object such as sand or hair down his windpipe, he would have a history of coughing.

I would suggest that you examine the dog before and after exercise to determine if the problem is aggravated by exercise. Then, perhaps gallop the dog over a longer distance, say 500 yards, to determine whether the problem is worsened after exercise. It is my opinion that if the problem is worsened by exercise, it would affect his performance potential.

I would suggest that you have the dog examined by a vet using a bronchoscope to check the lower windpipe and lung area. It may also be worthwhile consulting your vet regarding the use of a bronchodilating drug to help overcome any broncho-constriction that may be present after exercise.

Q **106.** **Please can you help with advice and information regarding a problem I have with my greyhounds; I am rather desperate at this moment in time. I have three greyhounds; one retired, the other two are bitches of racing age. Both the bitches tore muscles in their shoulders at 16 months after some 16 races. I rested them for some time and then started to put some serious work into them.**

At this time, I noticed there was some slight dry sneezing, and one bitch would have a warm nose on occasions. I tended to ignore this as they were eating well, although I was not entirely happy with their general condition, although their weight remained stable all the time.

Anyway, I raced them and they ran well, both winning three of their first four races. I was still not pleased with their condition but a lot of little things I noticed I put down to lack of fitness.

On her fifth race, one of the bitches ran poorly and I could see the run had hurt her. She failed to eat all her food after the race, so I visited my local vet. He could find nothing wrong with her, other than that she had had a possible infection and was now recovering. He put her on a short course of antibiotics and said she should be OK. But the next time out, she ran terribly and was obviously distressed after the run. I decided to rest her. Three days later her breathing was coming in rasps, and my vet diagnosed bronchitis. A course of antibiotics brought no response whatsoever.

In the meantime, the other bitch was showing similar symptoms. The vet said it looked as if it was a virus. A blood test showed the blood was normal but the count was low; a condition which he told me was consistent with a long-standing virus. The bitches have improved slightly; their lungs are clear but their throats are affected with laryngitis symptoms. How long is a virus going to continue? Is it possible that something in their environment is causing it, although my retired dog was kennelled with me for three years and showed no symptoms, but he now has a bad throat and barks with a frog in his voice.

Their diet consists of 1 pint of powdered milk, 1 egg, 4 oz baked brown bread (each dog) for breakfast. Their main meal is 1/2 loaf of baked brown bread, 11/3 lb cooked beef, 12 oz of vegetables, varied with tripe occasionally. I use supplements such as SA37, Stress, Energy+, Vethealth Hyper Nutrient.

I have had working dogs all my life, but I am a novice with greyhounds. I have had four and they seem to be very troublesome dogs, but I have never experienced a virus like this

before. Any information and advice will be greatly appreciated as I am really concerned now that the bitches' racing careers will be ended before they have really started.

A I can certainly understand your concern since your greyhounds have had a chronic condition for some time. From your description it is not clear whether your dogs are suffering from chronic laryngitis during the recovery from an infection with kennel cough.

The lowered white cell count on the blood test does indicate that the dogs could be suffering from a long standing viral condition such as one of the viruses that make up the kennel cough syndrome. Unfortunately, specific treatment for this type of long standing laryngitis cannot be carried out. However, your vet may decide to take a swab of the tonsil and throat area to determine whether there is a germ build-up, and its sensitivity to antibiotics.

This would be particularly useful if your greyhounds have inflamed tonsils, and an accumulation of thick mucus in their throats. In many cases a daily dose of 1 tbsp of glycerine, fortified with 5 drops of menthol or 2 drops of tincture of iodine, can help to reduce the irritation in the back of the throat if no actual germs are isolated. Give this daily over the back of the tongue about 10 minutes before walking the greyhounds. If the greyhounds are coughing up phlegm from the back of the throat, your vet may prescribe Bisolvin tablet for 7-10 days.

The incidence of infection with the 'windpipe worm' is increasing in greyhounds. These worms irritate the lower airways to cause a chronic cough and poor performance. Your vet will check the lower airways with a 'scope' and prescribe treatment if these worms are present.

107. Q I own four greyhounds. Recently they started coughing so I took them to my vet who took a swab from the throat and sent it to the lab for analysis. The result came back saying it was kennel cough. So far the vet has tried four types of tablets on them and there is no change. This has gone on for seven weeks. My vet said there is nothing else he can do, but told me to rest them for 3 months until it clears up.

The symptoms are as follows: swollen tonsils, white froth in the back of the throat, and coughing first thing in the morning after feeding and after light walking. The tablets he has tried are Tribesen 80, Ceporex, Vibromycin 50 and Linconeti.

I have only been walking them 3/4 of a mile twice a day with no running ,and I have been spraying the throat with dilute TCP three times a day. I hope you can come up with a solution for me.

A Recovery from the symptoms of kennel cough usually takes some time. Although antibiotics are helpful in the control of the bacterial germs associated with kennel cough, the inflammation and other damage to the respiratory tract may take some time to settle down. It is also questionable whether antibiotics given for respiratory conditions in the dog reach effective levels in the blood to be helpful in controlling the germs associated with this illness.

From your description the dog appears to be suffering from a tonsillitis and irritation in the back of the throat, persisting after the initial kennel cough infection. It may be necessary for your vet to take a further swab from around the swollen tonsils and determine if another antibiotic may be more likely to clean up the condition. Therapy with a drug to aid the removal of mucus and phlegm from the back of the throat may also help to hasten recovery. Your vet may prescribe Bisolvin or Torbutenol tablets, depending on the origin of the excess phlegm.

In some cases, it is not a good idea to suppress the cough, particularly when the lower airways are still congested. Also, many trainers find that 5 drops of menthol or 2 drops of tincture of iodine

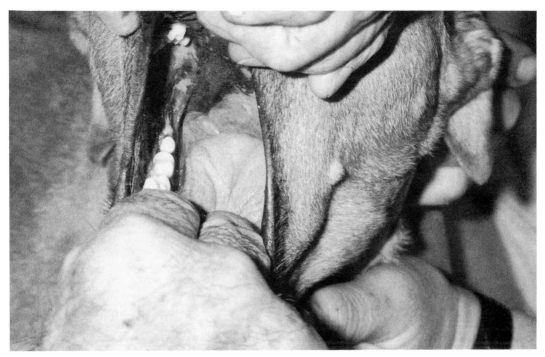

Check the tonsils on a greyhound that picks at its feed, froths at the mouth after a gallop, or has a cough when exercised. To examine, open its jaws and press down the tongue with the fingers to expose the tonsils. Severe tonsillitis, with engorged surface blood vessels should be referred to your vet for antibiotic treatment. Mild tonsillitis often responds to an antiseptic soothing throat lotion of 10ml of glycerine containing 2 drops of weak iodine solution (2.5 per cent tincture) squirted over the tongue daily, about 10 minutes prior to exercise or walking, for 5-7 days – no longer.

added to 1 tbsp of glycerine is helpful in clearing up the back of the throat. This can be given once daily over the back of the tongue, about 10 minutes prior to walking the greyhound. This treatment can be given daily for 10-14 days. However, in many cases kennel cough takes some time to clear up. Unfortunately, as your whole kennel has been affected, this generally increases the time for recovery.

Q I bought a greyhound 11 months ago. Three days after buying the bitch she started **108.** coughing, so I took her to my vet and he said she had tracheitis, and he gave her a course of antibiotic tablets, but they didn't cure the cough. So he tried her with another course of the same tablets, and they still didn't get rid of the cough.

I took her to another vet and he tried her on four more different types of antibiotics, but the cough still persisted. The vet then took a swab test from the dog's throat and had it analysed. The result was that she had septic tonsillitis caused by streptococcal infection, and he gave her a suitable course of antibiotics to stop this type of throat infection, but they also didn't work. He then decided to take her tonsils out followed by another course of antibiotics, but this didn't work either.

I then took her to another vet with a list of all the tablets she had had from the other vet. This vet tried her on three more different types of antibiotics she hadn't had, but still the cough persisted. The vet said there was not a lot more he could do to help us, as the bitch had had all the tablets for this type of throat infection he could think of.

All I can add to this is that the coughing never goes away completely when she is on a course of tablets. But it does get better, no matter which one she is on. If she is off the tablets for any length of time the cough gets bad and she goes off her food and loses weight. Before I bought the bitch she had three wins on her race card in the previous five weeks. Could you please help a desperate owner?

A   She certainly seems to be suffering from a chronic airway problem, probably as a result of a severe kennel cough infection. Considering your bitch has been rather unresponsive to treatment and that she has already had her tonsils removed, I would suggest that the underlying problem could be an irritation to the throat area, windpipe or even the upper part of the lungs. The streptococcal bacterial infection that you mention is not uncommon in dogs as a secondary infection following a virus.

Dusty straw or paper bedding may also irritate the airways and cause 'asthma' type symptoms of coughing and wheezing. A hammock type bed is recommended as it reduces dust and allergies. However, it usually clears up quite quickly with antibiotics and therefore, in my opinion, such a persistent cough is probably due to a physical problem in her airways.

In some cases, collapse of the windpipe where is enters the chest cavity can restrict the airway and cause coughing. In other cases a flap of lining from the windpipe may obstruct the airway and irritate it to cause the greyhound to cough. Therefore, I suggest you take your dog to your vet to have a full examination with a bronchoscope into the throat area, windpipe and lower airways to check for a physical injury or some other abnormality.

Your vet may also recommend an X-ray to check her lungs to ensure that they are not damaged in any way. In my opinion, a thorough physical examination of the bitch would be most important, particularly since she has not responded to antibiotics or other forms of medicinal treatment.

In some cases medication with a human cough medicine is useful in suppressing a persistent chronic cough. However, you should consult your vet for advice and dose rates before administering it to your bitch.

PORTA-MAG

PORTA-MAG treats injuries without passing electrical currents through the dogs body. It treats injuries without the need for sticky gels or water.
It treats all injuries without causing any discomfort or stress.
It treats the whole body whilst the dog is completely relaxed.

PORTA-MAG is a necessity in any kennel where greyhound racing is taken seriously.
It is produced by people who know the full extent of its capabilities through years of personal experience.
We are here to share that knowledge freely.

Often imitated – Never equalled

PORTA-MAG is the one machine that does everything a Greyhound man needs it to do.
Call us at any time to discuss your requirements.
You will not have to talk to an answer phone, someone will be here to talk to you personally.

£525.00 & £399.99

**Romar Electronics
Torne Gatehouse, Epworth,
Nr. Doncaster DN9 1LE   Tel: 0427 875004**

128

Chapter Five

BREEDING PROBLEMS

THE IN-SEASON BITCH

Q I have an eleven-month-old bitch, who is currently being schooled, and I am told that **109.** she should come into season at any time now. At what age does a greyhound bitch usually come into her first season, and is it possible to miss the signs, although I look every morning to see if colour is showing?

On the question of exercise, can a racing bitch be raced once colour has shown, and what form and amount of exercise is suitable when she is in season to keep her fit, without harming her in any way? Any information on what constitutes a suitable diet throughout the full season would be appreciated.

A Generally, bitches come into season not so much by age, but by their size. The smaller bitches may not start to cycle until they are 14-16 months of age, whereas the well-developed bitches usually start to cycle at an earlier age. However, you will find the bitch's behaviour will become more friendly, and the vulva will start to swell slightly as her season starts to cycle. Once the vulva shows obvious swelling and puffiness, then the bitch is usually in the first phase of her season.

Generally, it is unwise to race a bitch when she is in season, and this is not recommended by racing authorities. However, short hand-slips over 100-150 yards 2-3 times a week, plus the normal amount of walking, are usually adequate to keep the bitch fit without harming her in any way. The full cycle will last from 14-21 days, depending on the age of the bitch. When a bitch is in season it is obviously important to make sure she is kept secure from visits by prospective suitors.

As regards a suitable diet throughout the full season, then the normal diet would be recommended. However, if the bitch is not exercised as much, you could cut down on the amount of meat and dry food to maintain her bodyweight. Once the season is finished, increase the diet in accordance to her exercise level to avoid cramping and other metabolic conditions in the bitch.

Q We have a three-year-old bitch who has not had a proper season. Last December she **110.** drained for two days, swelled for two days, and then was back to normal. We took her to the vet and a slight infection was found. Antibiotics were prescribed, and the vet suggested we should have her spayed if there were any further problems.

We gave her a three month rest in case she came into milk, but she did not. Since coming

back to racing she has not shown the same ability over 700 yards, which was her best distance. Now she has come back into 'partial' season again. Please could you give us your advice.

A It is not uncommon for bitches that are bred for, and raced over longer distances to have abnormal cycles. It is considered that the stress of long distance racing and the time in training suppresses the normal hormone levels, and therefore these bitches do not cycle as intensely, or as regularly as sprint bitches.

As your bitch is getting older, it is unlikely that she would not be as competitive over longer distances as she would have been. However, she may be able to handle shorter distances and in doing so, reduce the stress on her body and therefore cycle more intensely when she comes into season again, possibly in twelve months' time.

If you plan to retire her and then breed from her, then I suggest that you discuss hormone therapy with your veterinary surgeon to attempt to bring her into season in six months' time. However, in many of these longer distance bitches, I have found that they do not cycle regularly for two or three years after they retire. If you wish to breed from a staying bitch, you should give her four to six months let-down from training before you commence attempting to breed from her.

111. Q **Can you please help me with a dietary problem for my bitch? Whenever she comes into season her appetite goes and she loses weight rapidly. Are there any major nutrients that I should particularly try to feed her, and is it worth increasing the amount of moisture in her feed? She seems to eat better when her food is sloppy.**

A It is not uncommon for greyhound bitches to go off their feed when they come into season. Generally, the diet should be made as nourishing and attractive as possible, once they become 'picky' in their eating habits. As your bitch loses weight rapidly, you should ensure that she gets adequate energy intake by providing extra fat in the diet. An extra two to three tablespoons of chicken, meat-trimmings or lard will increase the energy density of the food that she does eat, and therefore reduce the risk of her losing weight.

It is also important to add adequate moisture to her feed, particularly if she is on dry feed, so that she is more likely to eat it. If you are feeding raw meat, you may wish to cook the meat lightly, so that the odour of the warm, cooked meat helps to stimulate her appetite.

If she still fails to eat adequate amounts, then a course of B complex vitamins, such as in Rebound, or even an appetite stimulate such as Fortex, which contains caffeine, would be useful in helping to increase her appetite. In most cases, it is best to try a number of different feeds to suit her individual likes and dislikes during this time.

112. Q **I am writing concerning the problem of suppressed seasons. My bitch has four-monthly seasons, which obviously causes problems with the dogs in the kennel. After her last season, our local vet prescribed Ovarid (3 per day for 8 days). Since the course ended the bitch has been fine. The problem is in her racing; she is ten lengths slower, despite being in excellent physical condition. I have since acquired Methyl Testosterone pills (5mls), but I have not used these yet.**
Could you answer some questions for me on this subject please?
1. Are you aware of Ovarid affecting performance? If so, how long for, and will it affect future seasons?

2. Would it have been better to use the Methyl Testosterone tablets? Are their side-effects similar?

A Unfortunately, hormones such as Ovarid, whilst they are extremely useful and widely used in other breeds of dogs, in my experience often cause a loss of performance when given to greyhound bitches to suppress their cycles. Many bitches put on weight, and their performance drops away dramatically, as you noted, although they look physically fit and in good general health.

This is because these type of hormones act by increasing progesterone type compounds in the body, which is the hormone of pregnancy. Therefore, many of the side-effects of pregnancy develop, including loss of performance, once the bitch is given a course of treatment. With time, the effect of the preparation will decline and the bitch should regain her speed and performance.

However, in most cases experience has shown that injections of short-acting testosterone hormone, or Methyl Testosterone tablets, as you mentioned, are probably better to use to suppress the cycle in racing bitches. Male hormones such as these help to suppress the heat period without affecting performance. In some cases, bitches appear to be 'stronger' although in my experience male hormones do not enhance their performance above their normal ability.

The Ovarid effect will decline over a three to four month period. Unfortunately, sometimes bitches will return to season even quicker after treatment with Ovarid type compounds. The use of male hormones such as testosterone has to be controlled. Excessively high doses of these can lead to swelling of the vulva, and protrusion of the clitoris, and also low-grade womb infection. Therefore, the dose-rate is best advised by your own veterinary surgeon.

In my experience, testosterone type hormones have little effect on a bitch's future breeding potential, providing they are given at a safe dose that simply suppresses breeding cycles. Normally, it is best to start on the recommended dose, and if the signs of excessive hormone therapy such as enlarged vulva and clitoris develop, then it is best to reduce the dose in a step-wise manner by a quarter of a dose every three weeks, until the side-effects disappear.

Normally, slight swelling of the vulva is acceptable, and indicates that there is sufficient hormone to suppress the cycles. In most cases, bitches that are bred to stay over long distances usually only require about half to two-thirds of the dose to keep them from cycling.

Generally, anabolic type hormones given in tablet-form have an effect of depressing liver function if given continuously for long periods. This can result in loss of performance, appetite and slow recovery. I normally recommend injections as administered by your vet.

Q I would like advice about my bitch, who is aged two years and seven months. She has never been injured or had muscle trouble, and neither my vet nor an osteopath have been able to find anything wrong with her. She is out of breath for ten to or fifteen minutes after running, but does not cough or splutter. She is well walked, contests distances from 480-747m, and has always run well. **113.**

However, since being in season she has put on 6½lb. I have reduced this by 2lbs but she still needs to get rid of the rest quickly, as this is losing her spots in trials. Can you advise me of a correct diet?

This is a list of her supplements and meals: 1 15ml spoon of Thrive; 1 tbsp cod-liver oil; 1 tsp SA37; 1 tsp Electocell; 3 tbsp ascorbic acid; 1 vitamin E tablet; brewers yeast.
Breakfast: 2 Weetabix; 1 egg; half cup lamb's milk; 1 tbsp glucose,
Evening meal: 1 cup bran; ½lb fresh meat and minced raw vegetables – no bread mixer-

meal or biscuits, in order to try and reduce her weight.

She looks in great condition and her coat is like glass, but between the ribs and hind she is so fat you would think she was in pup, which she is not.

A From your description it is very likely that your bitch is suffering from a pseudo pregnant-type condition. In many cases, and particularly in greyhounds for some reason, bitches that come into season and are not mated frequently develop a false pregnancy-type condition. Although it is not fully understood, the hormone imbalance in these bitches causes their body to change and develop in the same way as it would if they were pregnant. Many bitches develop milk glands and start to run milk at about seven to eight weeks after their season. This could also account for her weight increase after being in season.

The diet you are feeding seems to be quite adequate, and should not result in such a dramatic increase in weight. The amount of cod-liver oil fed should be reduced to 2 tsp daily as, when combined with vitamin A and D contributed by SA37, excess of vitamins may cause bone and liver abnormalities. However, I would suggest that the amount of bran you are feeding is probably a little bit excessive, and I would cut that back to about half a cup. Excessive bran in the diet will increase the bulk of the stools and interfere with absorption and balance of essential calcium and other minerals.

Unfortunately, there is not much you can do once a bitch develops a false pregnancy. Generally, it is unwise to race these bitches because they lose tone in the ligaments of their pelvis just as they would in late pregnancy, and this can risk them developing an injury when galloping. I would suggest that you contact your local vet and have the bitch examined and obtain his opinion on whether she should be turned out for a month or so until she returns to normal.

114.Q **In July last year I sold a good, staying bitch that had just come into season. Talking recently to the buyer, he said she was useless, and I agreed to replace her. Thinking it over, I thought she might not be chasing the inside hare. However, the full story has now unfolded.**

When she was approximately six weeks in season the new owner took her to the vet and had her injected for worms. He ran her in a trial about ten weeks out of season, and she went very well, and over the next couple of weeks she made top grade. But at fourteen to fifteen weeks out of season she came into milk. He took her to the vet, who suggested she must have had a false heat – this was rubbish as she was in season when I sold her.

After a month's rest he started to race her again, but she got slower each time she ran. I feel the vet was wrong to inject a bitch when in season. However, my main concern is the bitch, and will I be able to race her again? I feel the injection badly interfered with her cycle and her metabolism. Would you agree? If so, could you advise on how I should treat her. Apart from this problem she looks very well in herself.

A From your description, there was approximately a sixteen-week time span from her initial season to when she produced milk. It appears to be a rather elongated false heat, but it may be as a result of her change in feeding, management and other stresses that contributed to the delayed onset of milk.

It is difficult to associate the worming injection with the alteration of her normal cycles. To my knowledge, there have been no published reports on the effect of worming injections on altering the cycles in bitches. However, in racing bitches, stress and other factors have been known to delay the onset of milk and also interfere with the regularity of cycles. As far as treatment is concerned, I would suggest that you treat her as you would normally treat a bitch in milk. This usually involves cutting back her work, and reducing her feed to a fifty per cent maintenance ration, and provide her with only a small amount of water per day to help dry out her glands. For this bitch, I would not recommend the use of hormones to try to dry her up quickly, since she may already have an imbalance of natural hormones. From your description of her performance, she obviously has some ability, and with time, she should regain her former performance.

Q I own a two-and-a-half-year-old greyhound bitch, which I bought at the Cradley **115.** Sales. After racing her successfully for nine months, she came in season. When she had been in season about eight days I became worried about the amount of blood she was losing, and at the same time she was refusing to eat her food. Ten days into her season I weighed her, and she had lost 5lb in weight. I visited my local vet who confirmed that the bitch was in season, but that it was unusual that she was not swollen and she could not possibly be mated. The vet put her on a course of antibiotic tablets.

It is now ten weeks since she came in season, but I have been unable to put back the weight she lost. I have wormed the dog for both round and tapeworm, and also increased her food, but without success. I have also tried your diet suggestions that I had previously read about – but again, without success. I would be grateful if you could give your opinion on the unusual season and the loss of weight that resulted from it.

At present, I am feeding my bitch two meals a day:
8.a.m: 1/2 pint milk and 2 Weetabix.
5 p.m: 1lb fresh meat, 4oz wholemeal bread (toasted), 4oz vegetables, plus a handful of biscuits.

A From your description, it appears that the bitch may have ruptured a blood vessel in her womb when ovulating, which resulted in internal complications. This may have been the reason why she refused to eat due to pain, or internal blood-loss. This may also explain the reason why she lost weight while in season. You say she did not have the normal signs of swelling of the vulva associated with heat, and that tends to confirm she may have had an internal injury or excessive bleeding of the womb.

I would suggest that you have her thoroughly examined by your vet once again to determine if she has any long-term internal damage. Usually it can take up to two to three months to regain weight after an internal injury. You do not mention whether she still refuses to eat sufficient amounts of food, as this may also reduce the likelihood of her regaining weight after her ordeal.

For breakfast I would suggest you feed her 1/2 a pint of milk, 2 Weetabix and 1/2 a cup of dry food. I would also suggest that you give her 1/2-1 cup of dry food during the middle of the day. This could be moistened with water, flavoured with a beef cube or 1/2 tbsp honey mixed in 1/2 a cup water and poured over the dry food. If she is a poor eater I would suggest that you grate a small amount of cheddar cheese over the food to entice her to eat. Increase the amount of meat in the evening meal to 11/4lb, the vegetables to 11/2-2 cupfuls, and dry food or biscuits to at least 1-11/2 cupfuls.

I would also suggest that you add 1-11/2 tbsp of lard to her diet to increase the fat intake, and also encourage her to put on more weight. Ensure she is on a vitamin/mineral supplement such as Feramo, and also 1-2 anti-stress tablets daily, such as Rebound, would be useful during the convalescent period.

If she starts to put on weight then I would suggest that you cut back on the dry food until she maintains her body weight and is ready to go back into training. Check her regularly for discharges from the vulva, just in case she has a developing womb or bladder infection. Seek immediate advice from your veterinary surgeon should you detect any abnormality.

MATING AND CONCEPTION

116. Q **I recently discovered that in Australia artificial insemination is permitted by the ruling body. I understand that it took quite a fight to get AI legalised. Could you tell me, have the critics been silenced by its success and what do you, as a vet, think of it?**

A The main advantage of AI is that a mating can be carried out despite problem behaviour of the bitch or dog; it can also be successful if the dog or bitch has sustained other physical injuries. AI is also known to increase the number of pups sired by an ageing or old stud dog with a proven track and breeding record. Recent technology has enabled semen to be frozen and stored for up to three to four weeks.

The other main advantage is that it reduces the risk of spread of venereal diseases in greyhounds, which generally are of fairly low incidence. Certainly, with the advent of long-term storage of frozen semen in the future, preservation of top-performing family lines will be possible for up to twenty to thirty years after a stud dog has died.

The general disadvantages are centred around the amount of technical expertise required, and the possibility of a limited number of top greyhounds dominating the industry. This could create abnormal demand for top bloodlines, which could sap the livelihood of many of the smaller breeders. It is also essential that accurate records be kept of AI in greyhounds to prevent abuses, and ensure the true bloodlines are maintained.

Despite the advantages and disadvantages, most breeders in Australia are using AI in greyhounds that otherwise could not be mated successfully. This includes very aggressive or timid bitches, stud dogs with limited fertility, and bitches that have had previous breeding problems and have been difficult to 'get in whelp'. In Australia the AI technique has to be managed by a veterinary surgeon at the time of the collection and insemination so that accurate records are kept, and the proper AI technique is carried out.

The main criticism appears to have been the dominance of certain stud dogs, and also the extra fees involved in veterinary supervision of the matings. However, by and large, only top stud dogs are regularly being used for AI and, in general, natural breeding is still widely used in breeding greyhounds in Australia.

117. Q **My bitch is due to break season any time now and I want to ensure that she is best prepared to conceive. Is there anything specific that I should or should not do? What are the values, for example, of courses of antibiotics or vitamin E to ensure that she is at her optimum?**

A Obviously, the bitch should be on a well-balanced diet with adequate amounts of energy and protein, and she should be exercised on a regular daily basis over 1-2 miles with occasional short hand-slips over 100-200 yards, just to keep her physically fit. Obviously, she should be in good physical condition without excess bodyweight.

A supplement of vitamin E, such as 200iu White-E daily, may be useful when given up to four weeks prior to the onset of the breeding cycle, to help aid fertility in brood bitches. However, when initially introducing a natural vitamin E, such as White-E, to the ration, it is best to start on 1/4 the normal dose initially, building up over a period of 10-14 days, as some greyhounds will become lethargic and go off their feed if suddenly introduced to the normal doses of natural vitamin E, without a step-wise build-up. Your bitch should also be wormed about three weeks prior to breeding, to ensure she has maximum nutritional efficiency.

As regards courses of antibiotics, if she is a maiden bitch then there is normally no need to give her antibiotics. However, if you are concerned that the colour of the discharge in the first few days is darker than normal, which could indicate a low-grade womb infection, then I would suggest that you have the bitch checked and a swab taken by your vet to see whether she has an infection.

Generally, it is unwise to treat with antibiotics unless there is a specific infection present in the bitch. It is also important to ensure that the antibiotic is tested for sensitivity against the infection, otherwise the antibiotic may select for other germs in the breeding tract, and these can cause build-up infection and abortion of puppies after mating.

I would ensure that she is on a vitamin E supplement through her pregnancy, as well as calcium supplements, preferably also containing vitamins A and D, to ensure that the developing puppies obtain maximum bone-building nutrients.

Q I have an open race marathon bitch who has just retired, and I want to breed with **118.** her. She came in season twelve months ago, so I took her to the stud dog. After twelve days she was still bleeding. The owner of the stud dog said she had had a good mating, even though he would not let me see it. However, she had no pups. She came in season twenty-five days ago, but she has not stopped bleeding for all of the twenty-five days, and has never looked ready for mating, so I have lost another twelve months. Is there a problem with her?

I understood that when a bitch first showed blood it indicated that she was two days into her season, so I calculated that in another ten or eleven days' time she should be ready for mating. But my bitch just bleeds for about twenty-five days and then dries up.

All the time she has been in season she has been kennelled with a dog, and the dog has never bothered her. Is she actually in season if the dog is not bothered? Twelve months ago when she was mated, she was still bleeding, and she was kennelled with the dog right up to the day she was mated. I am desperate to find out the problem so I can mate her next time around. Can you please help me?

A I suggest you have your bitch examined by your vet in about six months time. Many staying bitches require a couple of seasons before regaining their fertility and settling to normal cyclic patterns. It is not uncommon for bitches to bleed for their full season. In fact, some bitches show very little colour. Likewise, the time of ovulation in a bitch can also vary. However, it is usual for a bitch to be ready to mate from about the tenth day to about the fourteenth day.

The usual signs for mating are softening of the vulva and the discharge becoming more 'straw' coloured. The bitch is also more receptive towards a male dog at this time. This can vary in individual bitches; some may not show signs of ovulation until as late as sixteen to eighteen days into the season, and will be receptive to the the dog at that time.

One of the best ways to assess when the bitch is ready is to have an experienced and proven stud dog on hand, who by nature knows when the 'time is right'. An experienced dog quite often will not have anything to do with the bitch until she is fully ovulating. A young, inexperienced stud dog, or a male racing dog, will often take little notice of difficult bitches.

You should also have your bitch checked by your vet, at which time swabs can be taken to check for infection, such as E.Coli, BHS, etc. Bitches can often carry a uterine infection which can have a detrimental effect on their fertility.

Tests can also be carried out to assess the stage of ovulation, or possibly the fertility of the bitch, based on blood progesterone hormone tests. It may also be a good idea to have a fertility check on the stud dog which you intend to use on your bitch. If the dog is used at stud regularly, as well as for racing, it may have the effect of lowering his sperm cell count. Time and a well-balanced diet should help him recover his potency.

119. Q **A friend of mine acquired an open-class bitch for breeding, and we tried mating her with my dog. The bitch appeared to be ready and willing, with her tail to the side, but my dog was not interested. We then tried her with two other young, healthy dogs with the same result.**

This bitch had been getting injections to prevent her breaking into season, and I was wondering whether the injections could prevent her emitting the odour which stimulates the dog?

A It is not uncommon for bitches that have been injected with hormones to prevent them coming into season during racing to react in this way. In many cases these bitches never develop swelling of the vulva, even when on heat. Although they appear to have a normal cycle with bleeding, they do not have the odour that attracts the stud dog.

In most cases it is best to take the bitch for a walk, allowing her urinate two or three times, and then allow the stud dog to walk over the same area to smell the urine patches. This will often cause a stud dog to become more excited if the bitch is in season, and, hopefully, he will mate her successfully.

Another practical method is to obtain some urine from another bitch in full season and distribute that around for the stud dog to smell before mating. You can also spray some of this bitch's urine over the rear and around the vulva of the bitch that will not take the dog, and this will help to attract the stud dog, and hopefully result in a successful mating.

If these remedies fail, then I suggest that you contact your vet and have the bitch thoroughly examined, in case she has other internal problems that are preventing her accepting the stud dog.

120. Q **Could you please give me advice on trying to breed from my greyhound bitch. She is a former, top open-class marathon racer, and was retired early due to a fractured wrist. She came into season for the first time at two and a half years old, and then for the second time, thirteen months later. When she was mated, a swab test was taken on the first day in season, and proved positive. She was put on a course of antibiotics to clear an infection, taken back to the same stud dog and left again for one week. She was given two more swab tests and was mated on the fifteenth day. She missed again.**

Now I wonder:
a) Is there any way of finding out if the bitch is fertile?
b) Is there any point in having swab tests, and would the antibiotics have any effect on fertility or mating?

c) Would there be any point in having the bitch brought into season at six months (she is a twelve-months bitch?
d) Can bitches take fertility drugs as women can?

A It is not uncommon for many marathon or 'staying' bitches to have difficulty in coming on heat after being retired from racing. It is thought that many of these bitches, due to the strength and stamina required for the long distance racing, may have higher levels of male hormones naturally in their system. In my experience, it is usually the better-performed bitches that have difficulty in coming into season. It could be related to their higher levels of natural, male hormone, and also the continuous stress of racing, which tends to suppress their breeding cycles.

As regards your query about problems that you have encountered with your bitch, provided the bitch has had the adequate course of antibiotics, then there should not be any problems with low-grade infection causing a failure of conception. It could be that there is a problem with the stud dog rather than the bitch, in this particular case, since you have mated her to the same dog. I take it for granted that the dog himself has had a good fertility record.

As regards finding out whether a bitch is fertile, obviously the most common way is to obtain conception from a mating. However, assays of hormones such as progesterone can be taken, which can give an idea of the time of ovulation and in some cases can be used to assess whether the bitch has normal hormone levels, which could be important for breeding. If the bitch has no obvious discharge and appears healthy in every way, then there is probably no need to take swabs to check for bacterial infection. However, you may wish to take swabs to check on the cell structure of the vaginal lining, which can help your vet to assess the proper time for mating.

I would suggest that you consult your vet as regards artificially bringing the bitch into season at say, six months after her last season. Various hormones can be used to bring bitches into season. If she fails to come into season with hormone treatment then a surgical operation to open the bitch up and massage her ovaries seems to give good results in many bitches that fail to come into season easily, or in some cases conceive readily.

As far as trying to stimulate fertility, then various hormone drugs are available to control the cycle of breeding. Over the years supplements of vitamin E, such as White-E, 200iu per day for up to six weeks or so, have also proven to be of use in difficult-to-breed bitches. I suggest that you have your bitch thoroughly examined by a veterinary surgeon that specialises in breeding dogs, preferably greyhounds.

BROOD BITCH/PUPPIES

Q I have a bitch due to come into season at any time and I intend to breed with her. **121.** Could you please advise me of the correct time to worm her with, if possible, some idea of the best type of wormer to use. How often should I worm the pups, and at what ages?

A Most breeders worm their bitches out on a regular basis until they come into season. Some worm out on the first day of the season, but in most cases the first regular worming should be adequate.

Your vet may advise you to worm the bitch again about six weeks after mating to clean her out before whelping. There are a lot of worming preparations available, but a broad spectrum wormer used as directed should be safe. Consult your own vet for specific advice.

When retiring or purchasing a bitch for breeding, suitability for breeding should not be taken on performance history alone, but also strength, type and conformation should be considered. The bitch illustrated was a highly successful racer, with good overall conformation that helped ensure continued soundness over her long racing career.

The whelped bitch should be wormed out again after a week or so, and puppies should be commenced on a regular weekly worming programme, usually with a syrup-based wormer, from fourteen days of age, depending on the preparation. Again, your own vet will advise you on the best programme for your particular needs, based on the infection rates in your kennels.

122.Q I have had a greyhound bitch since she was a pup of twelve weeks. She is very well-bred and she has been a good servant to me. I tried to take a litter from her when she was five years old, but she missed. This year I took her to a stud dog and she had a beautiful litter of eight dogs and two bitches. The problem is that she had, what the vet called, mastitis in her milk so eventually we lost eight of the pups. I went by the book – by worming, swab test, etc., and as I said the pups were big, strong and healthy. Is there any way she could have another litter or will we always have this problem?

A In most cases mastitis is a temporary condition, and providing it is treated early there should be no long lasting effects on the bitch's milk glands. However, if the glands appear to be enlarged and have lost their normal soft consistency, then there is a chance that internal damage has been done to the milk-producing tissue. In this case the bitch would have less chance of producing adequate milk to feed her litter.

The risk of mastitis may be reduced prior to her next litter by giving her a course of antibiotics, prescribed by your vet, during the last week or so before she is due to whelp. This may reduce the risk of germs creating mastitis if an infection was the main cause of the original problem. You could put your bitch back into whelp and arrange for a foster bitch, or hand-rear the puppies on a suitable milk replacer diet.

Alternatively, I suggest that you have your bitch thoroughly examined by your vet once the pups have been weaned, to decide whether she has adequate gland area still viable for producing milk.

Q **My brood bitch is five and a half years old, and I have had one litter from her. There 123.** **was only one pup and this was delivered by caesarian operation. The vet said it was a** **large pup and there was not enough pressure to open the way for the pup.**

The bitch in question is a twelve-month bitch, and I wonder whether or not it would be safe to breed from her again when she breaks again. If so, will she have a normal litter and delivery or will she have to have another operation.

Finally, can you tell me if, after only having one pup in the first litter, is there any reason why she could not have a normal litter of four to six puppies?

A It is not uncommon for a large pup to be delivered by caesarian operation for the reason that your vet explained. However, there are various reasons why your bitch may have had only one pup. This may have been due to poor fertility of the dog, or other internal womb problems of the bitch herself.

If the fertility of the dog was the underlying reason, she would be able to conceive more pups when you next put her to stud. If you intend using the same dog again, then you should query the dog's fertility history, depending on his mating frequency, his age, and any other information on the fertility that the owner or veterinary surgeon may be able to offer.

Generally, there should not be any reason why you should not be able to breed from her again when she breaks. The caesarian operation does not generally damage the uterus, and the bitch should be able to have a normal litter of pups. However, if the bitch has an internal womb or ovarian problem then it may be difficult to forecast the result of the next mating. Your vet who did the original caesarian may be able to provide a further comment on whether her breeding organs were normal. If she does conceive a large litter, then there is no reason why she should not be able to whelp them naturally, since she is a relatively young bitch.

I would suggest that your bitch is checked by your vet prior to mating. It may also be a good idea to supplement her with vitamin E, such as 100iu of White-E daily, for four to six weeks prior to when you expect her to break. Therapy with vitamin E, combined with a thorough check by your veterinarian, should give her the best chance of having a fertile break.

Unfortunately, many bitches that only have one break per year often have a small litter after their first mating. In most cases, unless there is some internal problem with the bitch or a fertility problem with the dog, then there is no reason why she should not have four to six pups. Consult your vet for further advice if necessary. Let's hope the next litter is larger, and that you get pups with good racing potential.

124.Q My bitch has just whelped a litter. She is very well-bred, and in her racing days she was a top-class stayer and won many opens over the longer trip. Nine months ago she was taken to be mated, but she would have nothing to do with my first-choice stud dog, and so I took her to another dog. It took quite a while before they actually mated and, unfortunately, nothing came of it.

We returned nine months later and left her with the stud dog's owner. This was more successful, and she had her pups four days ahead of schedule. The first four were fine; all strong and healthy, although she had a little trouble as she would not stand while having them. For the next three hours nothing happened, and I became very worried. But then she had another pup, followed by a second one five minutes later. She cleaned herself up, had a drink and went outside, so we thought she had finished.

The next day at 12 noon – thirteen hours later – she had another pup, which was born dead. Immediately the vet was called; he examined her and said that there was at least one more dead pup inside. He gave her an injection to help make her womb work and luckily she got rid of those remaining – three more – without too much trouble. Unfortunately, two of the original pups died the next morning as they looked very weak. To cap it all, the bitch did not have a lot of milk so we are now hand-feeding them every two hours. I am glad to say the remaining four pups look great – big, strong and healthy.

I would never put her through all this again if I thought there was a likelihood of her having as much trouble. But could you explain why she had so much trouble and if a second litter would cause the same amount of discomfort to her?

A It is indeed bad luck that she only had four live pups out of a possible ten. There are various reasons why bitches have difficulty in delivering all their pups. In most cases, dead pups such as she had, half-way through her whelping, would interfere with the whelping process. Many owners get their bitch examined by a veterinary surgeon before they whelp to find out how many pups the bitch should deliver. If there are a lot of pups, an X-ray is useful in determining the viability of all the pups, and it can help to predict whether there is going to be a problem. Your own vet would be able to give you more advice on this specific matter.

In many cases, the muscles of the womb get fatigued, and therefore do not continue the whelping process. This may help explain why she did not recommence whelping until next day. This may have reduced the viability of the pups, particularly when the whelping process is prolonged and there is blood supply problems to the womb. Generally, bitches on their second litter do not have any whelping problems. However, individual problems do occur in certain bitches, and can cause similar discomfort in successive litters.

I would recommend that you have your bitch thoroughly examined by your vet within two weeks of her whelping date to ascertain the number of pups, and also whether there could be any difficulty in delivery. If there is a delay during the whelping process, I would recommend that your vet examines the bitch and perhaps give her the hormone to contract her womb to speed whelping. Again, your vet would be able to give you more specific advice at the time. It is good to hear the remaining four pups are doing well, and let's hope they make champions on the race track.

125.Q I have a top-class brood bitch who has had three litters of pups, producing top-class open racers. But the last three times that she came in season she only stayed on heat for eight to ten days, and then dried up. The bitch comes in season once a year and she is now eight years old.

A It is not uncommon for an aged bitch to miss cycles or develop less intense cycles, which fail to culminate in a fully fertile cycle. Since your bitch has already had three litters of good pups, every effort should be made to try to determine the underlying problem.

In the last month or so before she is expected to come into season next time, I would ensure that she is on a balanced diet without being too fat, and receives exercise of 1-2 miles daily. The addition of a daily supplement of vitamin E (200iu White-E daily) may help to increase her overall fertility, particularly if she has been maintained on a frozen meat-based diet with low levels of vitamin E. Start on a dose of 50iu vitamin E daily, increasing to 200iu daily over 10-14 days.

When she comes into season it may be worthwhile having her thoroughly checked by your veterinary surgeon. However, because she is an aged bitch, then it may be that her ovarian function has declined, and therefore treatment with hormones to stimulate egg release may be useful. In younger bitches that have failed to produce a fertile season, it has been found that operating to open the bitch up and stimulate the ovaries by either massage or pin-pricking the

TRAINER'S TIP

A calcium supplement, such as Calci-D as illustrated, should be added to the diet of older brood bitches in proportion to the amount of meat in the diet. Older bitches over 6-7 years of age are unable to absorb calcium as efficiently as younger greyhounds. All growing and racing greyhounds must be given supplementary calcium to balance high meat based diets.

Greyhound puppies usually weigh between 14-16oz at birth, and they gain weight rapidly in the first few weeks.

ovary surface does help to increase the fertility of the season and the conception-rate in these bitches. However, it would be up to your own veterinarian to decide what would be the best way to handle her case.

126. Q **Could you please tell me what a good weight is for a greyhound pup at birth? I was amazed to see seven pups whelped by 56 lb bitch, sired by a 62lb dog. The heaviest was 1lb 12 oz, the smallest 1lb 8 oz. No one else who I have spoken to has ever weighed pups at birth.**

A Greyhound pups should weight between 14-16 oz at birth. Bitches generally weigh 1-2 oz less than dog puppies. Obviously the bigger the litter, the smaller the relative size and birthweight of individual pups. There is also variation between individual pups in a litter. Puppies that are conceived in the wider part of the womb are usually larger than ones conceived at the extremities of the womb tubes.

The birthweight of your puppies certainly seems to be much higher than the average expected for a greyhound pup. Birthweights of other breeds, particularly the heavier breeds of dog, do reach 1 1/2-1 3/4 lb in many cases. If your scales are correct, then you certainly have a very heavy litter of pups. Let's hope that the bitch will be able to care for and feed them all to ensure they grow and mature to well-boned and developed racing greyhounds. You may need to supplement the pups with milk at two weeks of age if they appear to be hungry and 'draining' the bitch.

Milk production in nursing bitches often drains the system of vital nutrients and calcium, and they may be more prone to stress conditions when they return to the rigours of racing.

As you observed, most greyhound breeders do not weigh pups at birth. However, if pups are lower than 9-10 oz in weight they are usually less viable and need extra feeding and care to ensure they survive the first month after whelping.

Q **I have a greyhound bitch who has had nine pups which are due to be weaned from her 127.
in about two weeks. I know time and rest are important, but is there anything else I
should do to get her body in shape for racing as soon as possible?**

A In most cases, after a bitch has had a litter of pups, then in my experience it is best to
introduce her to light exercise on the lead for about four weeks, to help her dry up her milk
and tone up her general system.

After the first two to three weeks, the bitch could be hand slipped over 100 yards two or three times a week to stimulate her blood production and general strength of muscle. After about six weeks of walking and short gallops, the bitch can be introduced to longer hand slips and short trials, particularly up a straight to try to build up her muscles and fitness. Depending on her general muscle development, then jogging the bitch on a lead up slight slopes will also help to strengthen her back and hind leg muscles for galloping.

Milk production in bitches often drains their system of vital nutrients and calcium, and therefore when they go back into work they may be more subject to stress conditions. Also, as calcium may have been reabsorbed from bone to maintain milk levels, these bitches may be more prone to toe and small bone fractures and other injuries. Therefore, ensure the bitch is on a vitamin and mineral supplement, such as Feramo-Greyhound, containing vitamins A, D, iron and other minerals, and also an additional source of calcium in her food, such as Calci-D. At least 2 tsp of calcium powder per day added to her feed would be required to rebuild skeletal reserves if they have been depleted during lactation.

It would also be a good idea to put her on to a vitamin E supplement, such as 100iu of White-E daily, as this will also help to strengthen her muscles and prepare her for racing. Depending on the bitch's milk gland development, you may find that you have to extend the time of initial training and conditioning so that she fully dries up her glands before she returns to active galloping.

146

Chapter Six

BEHAVIOURAL PROBLEMS

PSYCHOLOGY

Q The art of training greyhounds is kept largely secret by the few trainers who excel in **128.** their area. For obvious reasons the tricks of the trade are not all widely accessible, as those in possession of the knowledge wish to keep their information to themselves. I wondered whether the psychology of greyhounds has been investigated in any depth and if so, where this information has appeared.

Certain aspects of psychological training interest me. For example, with greyhounds being kept in large numbers and being constantly moved from kennel to track, or kennel to kennel, does this destroy their natural territorial instinct? This does wonders for their placid nature, but does it affect their mental state?

There also seems to be a great difference of opinion over how dogs should be handled. The old school of thought was to let greyhounds survive harsh weather in order to harden them up, and the belief was that playing with greyhounds and treating them softly, would turn them into fighters. Others say that because they love their dogs and treat them like pets, the dogs are happier in themselves and therefore healthier and better equipped to perform on the track. Which method do you find works best?

A psychological study of greyhounds would perhaps help with those dogs that are terribly shy and nervous. I am sure that the 'deep-end' theory (i.e. taking them to crowded places) works up to a point, but it cannot be the ideal way of solving nervousness.

A Your queries certainly are worth considering. To my knowledge, there is very little information on the psychology of the greyhound in training. It is well known that greyhounds tend to react favourably to human contact when being walked, and to being handled firmly without being harsh.

You raised a very good point about the travelling and grouping of greyhounds at races. Many consider that the refinement of the greyhound breed has led to a loss of strict territorial type instincts, and that greyhounds are really a fully domesticated dog. However, greyhounds will still show dominance and fight when brought together in groups where natural instincts can lead to disagreement.

Most modern greyhound trainers provide better living conditions for the greyhounds, rather than make them 'tough it out' in outside kennels and runs. The incidence of respiratory conditions and also their general performance improves when greyhounds are cared for, and housed in comfortable surroundings. The bond between greyhound and trainer is also important to many younger greyhounds particularly, and they seem to 'try' to perform their best. Gone are the days where greyhound trainers discipline their dogs harshly, and many women trainers seem to be able to get the best out of greyhounds where other trainers previously failed.

Certainly, in my experience, taking young greyhounds to trial tracks and meetings to accustom them to the crowd, appears to work. Obviously, this should be done on a 'stepwise' basis, without terrifying the youngster. Most greyhounds are 'gregarious' in nature, and prefer to have other greyhounds to frolic with in yards and small runs. The greyhound trained alone can become less competitive and, many consider, lose its pack instinct to chase the lure.

SEX DRIVE

129. Q **I hope you can help me with a problem I have with one of my greyhounds. The dog in question has raced and won at my local NGRC track when he was with a professional trainer. However, when I got the dog, I trialled him four days later and he gave up chasing and was wobbly at the pick-up. He also urinated blood, so I took him straight to my vet. He was on antibiotics for a couple of weeks and further blood tests proved negative. When I got the dog he was put in the same kennel as a bitch of mine, who was about 24 days in season, which I thought was safe to do. However, he tried to mount her and lick her and started ejaculating. With this happening I quickly separated them.**

This was three or four months ago, and now there is semen near his back hocks every day I get him out of the kennel. Also, when I walk him about three miles daily, he is very tired on returning and puffing very hard. The last thing I noticed was when he was in a race at an unlicenced track. He led at the first bend and along the far straight went 8 lengths clear. However, coming into the home straight he stopped chasing but still won by 4 lengths, although was slowing down. He has never given up before I had him, and he was a useful grader. He is four in October but sound and genuine, so could it be he is not chasing the outside runner now, or is this due to being with the bitch for that short period of time?

A Dogs sometimes will start to ejaculate themselves in the kennel overnight. If it occurs only occasionally it seems to have no ill effect on the greyhound's performance. However, if it occurs on a regular nightly basis, many trainers believe that it can tire the greyhound and it will lose 3-4 lengths in a race. It is not uncommon for stud dogs to serve bitches in the morning and race in the evening, without affecting the dog's performance.

The best form of treatment for this type of behaviour is an injection of female hormones over a two-week period. I suggest that you contact your vet on the use of a short course of a low dose rate of a female hormone to reduce your dog's sex drive. The history of the dog also suggests that he may have a problem with a low grade bladder infection. I suggest you also ask your vet to do a urine test to check the pH of the urine, and the presence of small crystals.

KENELLING PROBLEMS

130. Q **I am writing to you in the hope that you may be able to help. I have a greyhound, kennelled with a professional trainer, who is extremely fast when taken to a private track for a gallop. Yet when he is taken to the NGRC track, he is hopeless.**

Supplements of high does of natural vitamin E can help to calm the nerves of a 'bad kenneller' on race days.

At the private track we can walk him around until he goes in the traps, and then when the traps open he just flies. But at the NGRC track he has to be put into kennels, and this is where the trouble starts. The trainer says that when he is put in the kennel he starts playing up. When they fetch him out of the kennel for his race, the air in the kennel is unbearable and the dog is very distressed (we have had to withdraw him recently because of heat exhaustion).

I would like to know whether this could be down to hyperactivity – because of the type of food he is being fed – or if not, is there any way to calm the dog without breaking any NGRC rules? My trainer says that the best thing to do is sell the dog to an independent trainer who can take him to a track, where he will not need to be kennelled, but I hate to see the dog's obvious ability go to waste if we can do something else.

A Unfortunately, young greyhounds can become excited when kennelled prior to a race. In some cases, these youngsters settle down once they become more experienced. I think it is unlikely that the type of food he is eating would be causing this problem, particularly since he does not have the problem at a private track.

In some cases, if you can arrange to, have the greyhound kennelled at an NGRC track during the day for a few hours when there are few other dogs actually in the kennels. Perhaps the racing manager could arrange this for you. This will help to settle him down, and get him accustomed to being kennelled prior to a race. You could stay with him for a while and settle him down.

There are a couple of therapies that can be useful in calming nervy dogs. These include such preparations as Valium and Dilantin, and must be prescribed by your vet. Both these drugs are contrary to the NGRC rules, and cannot be used near to racing days. However, they are useful in helping to settle nervy greyhounds over a period of a week or so, in a decreasing dosage rate, to wean the greyhound off the medication. This type of medication is contrary to NGRC rules generally, and your own club would be able to advise you more specifically on this type of medication.

Supplements such as high doses of natural vitamin E, as in White-E, can be used to settle 'nervy' greyhounds prior to racing. Normally, only natural forms of vitamin E have a beneficial effect, and the greyhound must be given 2-3 times the normal dose on the morning before and the morning of the kennelling to help reduce excitement. As vitamin E is only a vitamin, there is no problem with normal club rules. I would suggest that you discuss these medications with your veterinary surgeon. It certainly would be a pity to relegate a good dog to racing on outside tracks.

131. Q Could you advise me if I can do anything to stop my bitch from wetting her bed. I have had her, and the dog, from pups. They are now 16 months old. I used straw until a couple of months ago when I changed to paper bedding. They are both kennelled together. The kennel is left open all day with a run, and they are only locked in at night.

They have the run for toilet purposes, but the bitch still goes on the bed to relieve herself and I have to keep changing the bedding. Now with summer coming on it will be worse for smell. I have tried vinegar on the bed, but to no avail. I have no such problems with the dog.

A From your description, the problem appears to have started when the bitch was in season earlier this year. Wetting her bed may have become a habit that she has developed since being in season, particularly as she may have been demonstrating her 'body language' to the dog. It may also be caused by irritation of the bladder following her season, due to a minor infection that gains entry through the bladder from the breeding tract. If she goes back to her bed to wet it, then it appears to be a habit rather than a need to urinate.

If you notice that she is urinating more frequently than normal, particularly when you are walking her and she squats down to pass small dribbles of urine, then you should have her checked by your vet for a possible bladder infection. It is not uncommon for young bitches to develop irritation in the bladder due to cystitis, or 'crystals'. The infection causes the formation of alkaline urine, which irritates the bladder and vagina, and causes the bitch to squat down more frequently because passing urine relieves the irritation.

However, if you think it is a habit developed during her season, then this may be more difficult to break. I would suggest that you change back to straw bedding for a little while to see if she still continues the habit. It may be that the paper bedding has some type of smell that encourages her to urinate on it. A sprinkle of citronella dropped on to the bedding may discourage her from sniffing it and then wetting on it. Alternatively, try to discipline her sternly if she attempts to wet on her bedding.

Q Due to conditions in my kennel being a little more cramped than I would like, I have **132.** had two dogs in the last month that have split the ends of their tails through over-exuberance at feeding time. I have bandaged the affected areas and muzzled the dogs to stop them removing the cover, yet they still seem to be able to shake off the bandage. I am worried that by tying the bandage any tighter, I may cause damage to their tails. Is this likely and if so, what can I do?

A It certainly is a problem in 'tail-waggers', and the only successful treatment that I have found is to dress the wounds with a soothing medication, and if infected, an antibiotic cream obtainable from your vet.

One of the simplest ways to prevent tail-wagging is to apply a dressing to the end of the tail and then stick elastic adhesive bandage onto the hair about 2-3 inches from the end of the tail. Attach a length of cotton gauze so as to pull the tail down between the greyhound's legs, and tie the cotton gauze in a loop around the flank.

Another successful method to prevent the tail being knocked is to obtain a plastic hair roller of the type that has a central core with an outside plastic mesh. This can be put over the end of the tail and then attached to the tail hairs with adhesive bandage. Even if the dog continues to damage the tail by wagging, then normally the outside of the plastic hair roller will protect the end of the tail.

This seems to be one of the better ways of helping to aid healing as well, as in many cases bandages tend to make the end of the tail 'moist' and this can delay healing. In most cases it is better to try to use a drying antibiotic spray to encourage healing. Should the greyhounds continue to bruise and bare the tips of their tails, then I suggest that you consult your own veterinary surgeon regarding a suitable treatment.

Q I am having a problem with my three-year-old greyhound dog, and I would be very **133.** grateful for any advice you can give me. In the morning is the worst time when I get him out of his bed for a walk before breakfast. He shakes himself very forcibly, to the extent he has broken his tail twice by banging it on the wall of the kennel. The lobes of his ears were also bleeding and sore as a result of this excessive shaking, but I have nearly got the ears cleared up.

I have taken the dog to my vet who is very helpful, but he cannot discover the cause or stop this shaking. He examined his ears inside and out and said they were clean with no mites or excessive wax. He gave me drops for his ears which I have been using. I have washed the dog three times; the first time using Alugan, the second time, the night before I swabbed him all over the Benzol Benzate, and the next day I bathed him using saline shampoo. The third time I washed him with a dermatology shampoo. I dried the dog thoroughly every time, finishing off with a hair-drier. The dog's skin is very flaky and after brushing him all over to remove as much as possible, I rubbed him all over with baby oil.

I had the dog bedded in ordinary shredded office paper as the cellophane is difficult to obtain. I have now removed this from his night kennel and small outdoor kennel, and I now

have continental quilts for my two dogs to lie on. My two dogs, both fed exactly the same, yet only the one is affected with this really annoying problem.

A It is not uncommon for greyhounds to shake themselves when getting out of their beds. Certainly, excessive wagging of their tails can lead to splitting of the tip of the tail. However, the type of shaking that you describe is not common, and could be related to a behavioural problem. It is most important to ensure that the greyhound's ears are clean and free of mites, and also any skin allergies are treated. This should remove any obvious irritation or stimulus to shake.

It could simply be a habit that the greyhound has developed over a period of time. In this case, I would have the greyhound carefully examined over the head and body area by your veterinary surgeon. Your veterinary surgeon may also prescribe a mild sedative such as Phenytoin, which may settle the greyhound and reduce any stimulus to shake himself after waking up. A short course is useful to settle down nervy greyhounds, and even those with 'fits' or other odd nervous behaviour.

134.Q **Could you please give me advice about my 21-month-old bitch. She is fed breakfast at 7.45 a.m. and her main meal at 4.45 p.m. She is walked before breakfast and again at 6 p.m. She has warm milk and water at 9.45 p.m. During the night she has the habit of eating her motions; we put a box muzzle on each night but she still gets it. She is not hungry because she tries to do it straight after the main meal.**

She was wormed and tapeworm was found. I wormed her again with worm tablets for all worms, and nothing showed. She has already won her first race for me, and everyone commented on how well she looked.

At breakfast she has 3 Weetabix with vitamins. Her main meal is 8oz dry feed (soaked for 6 hours), 1lb minced beef - cooked chicken twice a week - and a vitamin and mineral supplement and Calci-D, 4oz cabbage and 2oz carrot. One other thing I do have is Ironcyclen liquid. Do I need to add this to the main meal?

A Unfortunately, it appears that your bitch may have got into the habit of eating her motions through being confined to kennels. From your description of feeding, you certainly look after her very well, and she appears to be obtaining plenty of fibre from the diet. Lack of fibre in the diet is one of the reasons some greyhounds start to eat their droppings.

There are various remedies to stop this habit. It appears that an injection of vitamin B12, which would need to be given by your vet, can help stop some dogs eating their manure. Normally, you would need to have your bitch injected twice a week with 1-2ml of vitamin B12. In theory, injecting vitamin B12 works on the principle that the dog is not absorbing the B12 produced in her bowels, and therefore eats her manure to obtain her supplies. However, the addition of Ironcyclen liquid which you have, provides Cobalt, which may help the greyhound to manufacture her own B12 in her large bowel during digestion. You could try this, and she should stop eating her droppings if this is the problem, over a week to 10 days.

The other method is to give the dog a dose of a substance that makes her manure unattractive. Over the years many trainers have reported that a cup of corn oil (maize oil) added to the diet, or administered over the back of her tongue with a syringe, will be effective in many cases. I have had good success with this method, as it appears to make the droppings very oily and smelly, and most unattractive to the greyhound. Normally one treatment is sufficient, but you may need to give your dog a cup of corn oil twice, one week apart, to get the best results. Again, you may wish to consult your vet regarding this treatment.

However, where it is simply due to habit, it is very difficult to prevent. Although some greyhounds can be distracted by discipline, they usually go back to their old habits. Some trainers believe that greyhounds eat manure when they have an infection in the tonsils. You may wish to have a look at her tonsils, preferably before she has eaten her motions. As you describe, these greyhounds generally look well and perform well, and in many cases it can be put down to a simple habit. Perhaps try strict discipline and cleaning up her motions as soon as she has passed them, for 1 to 2 weeks. As regards adding Ironcyclen to the feed, it is best added to the evening meal.

BAD TRAVELLERS

Q As soon as my greyhound, who is two years old in October, enters the back of my estate car, he immediately starts frothing at the mouth – even before I have started the car. Then for a period of twenty minutes saliva pours from his mouth and nostrils. **135.**
I have tried the company of a bitch, but this has made no difference. This seems entirely connected with car travel, as he is usually in the last race and is perfectly docile and dry when he comes out of the kennel. Is there any solution to my problem?

A The problems of a bad traveller are difficult to solve. There are so many suggestions but the fact that there are so many so-called 'solutions' is evidence in itself that there is no single answer.

Most greyhounds are good travellers, although some will fret in the racing kennel. Your dog seems to do it the other way round, which from a racing point of view is a good thing. One solution is the administration of drugs, such as a tranquilliser to prevent salivation. I could not recommend such a procedure. It may create more problems than solutions.

You could try giving him a small sweet, milky feed just before the journey. This sometimes helps, especially if he is also prone to cramp. Perhaps give him a course of 100iu of vitamin E daily, e.g. natural White-E, for a week or so, and then give him 3 times this dose on the morning before and morning of travelling to help settle his nerves. Vitamin E may also make him perform better by improving his muscle stamina.

It may have something to do with your particular car; you could change it! Static electricity can have an effect on certain animals and an anti-static device such as a chain dangling on to the road can be effective. You mention that he starts frothing even before you start your car, which makes this theory less likely. But some animals may be upset by something such as static electricity that is associated with the car. Check the type of carpet in the back of the vehicle, and perhaps put a soft bed in the back for the greyhound to settle and rest.

The most satisfactory way of treating your greyhound is by using a training regime designed to dissociate the connection between your car and racing. The frothing at the mouth is anticipatory to a reward, in this case the pleasure of running, which all greyhounds enjoy.

Allow your greyhound to remain in your car for varying periods during the day when you are not going racing. Take him on various journeys, shopping etc., where the car journey is not associated with taking him to the track. He will gradually learn that the car is not always associated with a race or trial and he will accept it for what it is.

He will, of course, learn that those journeys that end at the stadium will be followed by a race and he will learn to recognise familiar scenery and get excited. But by that time you will be at the stadium, where you say he is usually quiet.

136. **Q** **I have a greyhound bitch of 17 months. She is a very bad traveller. I can get her to the track now without her being sick, but after the race she is violently sick – just like white foam. She is very distressed and loses about 2 lb. I had her on a course of Betacel but to no avail. The vet gave her Phenergan, to be taken the night before she raced. This did not help either. I have tried her with Milk of Magnesia and Glucodin, and have tried taking her to the track an hour before she races so that she might calm down. This doesn't work either. Can you help?**

A Because the bitch is relatively young, she may be nervous and insecure when travelling. It may be useful to travel a more mature and well travelled greyhound with her to help her become accustomed and settle down in the vehicle. Some greyhounds develop travel sickness when they are enclosed in a vehicle, and if possible, initially travel her in a more open vehicle such as an estate car with windows and plenty of fresh air, rather than in an enclosed van.

It is important also that she is kept on a physiological salt supplement, such as Betacel, to ensure that she does not dehydrate when travelling. One tsp a day in her feed would be adequate during the cooler months of the year. A half cup of Recharge drink offered on arrival at the track may also help to condition her for racing. In most cases, a course of treatment with Phenergan is useful, but you may need to give her a number of doses of this to let her become more accustomed to the travelling. If she gets stressed at the racetrack then it may be useful to take her to a trial track a few times, and mingle her with the crowd and other greyhounds so that she gets used to the general atmosphere of the racetrack. As an alternative, a course of treatment with sodium phenytoin, available from your vet, may also be useful in settling down this type of nervy behaviour. This medication is widely used in children, and the normal dose rate comparable from a child to a 30kg greyhound is useful when given morning and night for at least seven to ten days, during which the greyhound should be exposed to the types of excitement and travelling that would normally upset her. The medication has to be withdrawn at least 72 hours prior to racing, but you should do this under the direct advice of your own veterinary surgeon.

And lastly, high dose therapy with vitamin E is sometimes useful to calm down a nervy bitch for race day. It is best to start on about 25-50iu daily of natural vitamin E, such as in White-E, and then increase the dose over a period of 7-10 days to the normal daily dose of 100iu. Then on the morning before and the morning of a race or trial, increase the dose to 300-400iu to produce a quietening effect. Although this course of treatment may not be effective the very first time it is used, after two or three such courses many greyhounds tend to settle down, and race more consistently.Therefore, attempt a combination of making her more confident by travelling her with other greyhounds that are very quiet and used to travelling, and perhaps trying the medications outlined above.

NERVOUSNESS

137. **Q** **I purchased a bitch puppy at the age of four months; she is now nine months old. When I go to put the lead on her or brush her, she cowers and urinates, yet at no time has she been ill-treated. When I talked to the person I bought her from he said it is the**

breeding. When she is let off in the fields she runs about playing as though nothing is wrong with her. But as soon as I go to put the lead on, the same thing happens. Could you tell me if there is anything I can give her as she does not seem to be growing out of it?

A In most cases, this type of reaction and loss of bladder control is due to nervousness and immaturity. In some cases it is a habit that is learnt from other greyhounds, particularly if her mother was timid and had a similar habit when being handled.

'Puddling' can be conditioned by occasionally going for a walk with emptying the bladder, particularly where greyhounds are kept in small areas and they are taken out frequently to urinate rather than mess in their kennels. In your bitch's case it is most likely to be a bad case of nerves.

Perhaps you could try to condition her not to urinate by kennelling her with an older bitch, and try to teach by example that 'puddling' is not the normal reaction to handling and grooming. A preparation containing high levels of vitamin B1 and B2, available from your vet, may be useful in settling her nerves. Your vet may also prescribe a short course of tranquillizers, such as Valium or Phenytoin, which may help her gain control of her nervous habit.

I have heard of owners of other breeds of dogs letting their children handle and play with nervy pups to settle them down, as she may be frightened by human adults. Perhaps you could spend a lot more time with her, and that may settle her nerves. Unfortunately, I can offer no sure way of overcoming the problem.

Q **138.** I have a racing whippet, 27 lb. He is normal all week, but on race day, at the track, he becomes excitable. He pants and drools. His faeces are green and soft. His diet is an all-in-one racing food and vegetables, milk and cereal and biscuits last thing at night. He has no added vitamins, etc. How can I stop this nervous reaction, as I am sure he is not racing right with this lot going on inside him.

A Unfortunately, it is not uncommon for whippets to have a 'nervy' disposition. The diet you are feeding seems to be quite adequate to meet his needs. However, if his skin is in good condition and returns immediately after a 'pinch test', then you may be able to reduce some of the milk or fluid in his diet, which may reduce the risk of him developing a soft green scour. However, you must ensure that he is not dehydrated at the time of racing, otherwise this could affect his performance and cause other metabolic problems.

With time, many 'nervy' dogs settle down to race quite successfully. You may wish to take your whippet as a 'crowd spectator' for two or three trials or races, to get him used to the travelling and race day noises. As far as trying to settle him down prior to racing, then over the years the use of vitamin E in high doses pre-race seems to have a good effect in settling down some 'nervy' greyhounds. For a whippet a normal daily dose would be about 50iu of vitamin E, such as White-E, increasing to about 200iu on the morning before and the morning of a race or trial. One or two treatments like this are often useful to settle down a 'nervy' dog and enable him to race to his potential. Vitamin E has no drug-like effect and it is safe to use pre-race. Other herbal remedies are available and may be of use. I suggest that you take him to a track for two or three 'dummy' runs to get him used to the crowd and noise, and this may be useful in settling him prior to racing.

Q **139.** I have a 30-month-old dog. The hair on his back stands up on his back on a regular basis if he is racing at night. When this occurs he seems to be down in the dumps whether he races twice a week or is rested for a month – although it does not seem to

affect his performance on the track. I have tried changing his diet from meat, brown bread and vegetables to dry meal, e.g. Respond 2000. I have also tried different vitamins, e.g. SA37, Energy Plus, Swift 88, Ryte, blood tonic and other greyhound tonics, but it makes no difference.

A From your description, the problem could be related to the dog being frightened of race day noise and routines. Fear will make some dogs tend to 'cringe' and become quite depressed in their attitude. From your letter I understand that the greyhound still performs well despite the problem with the hair standing up on its back. In some greyhounds, heavy infections of hookworms will tend to give a dry looking coat which stands up in a slightly curled type fashion along the back of the greyhound. However, regular worming is recommended to overcome this problem.

In hot weather, or when the greyhound has a temperature due to a virus or some other underlying disease condition, the coat will sometimes become 'starry' and stand up along the back and neck. However, this would be obvious by the greyhound's depressed attitude. You could take the greyhound's temperature to find out whether it is raised above normal and consult your vet if it is elevated.

As far as changing diets, I do not consider the problem is related to the diet that the greyhound is presently being fed. It is more likely to be a problem related to the 'fear' of racing rather than typical excitement that occurs in some younger, less mature greyhounds

RACING STRESS

140. Q **My two-year-old greyhound bitch is making my life a misery. I paid £100 for her about four months ago. She was in poor health when I got her. It looked as though she had had a fall at the track as she had a large amount of cuts and scratches over her front and back legs. She also had a lot of hair missing from her hindquarters, elbows and chest.**

After taking her to the vet, who put her on a course of tablets, vitamins and cream, she looked a lot better. But I cannot seem to get her to liven herself up. Looking at her you would think she was hoping to die. You let her off her lead and she just stands there. I have had greyhounds for five years, and I have never had a dog who has done this. I am unemployed on a low budget, but I love my greyhounds. I must have spent over £100 on vet bills, and I just don't know what to do next. Would it be better to have her put to sleep?

She is on high protein food, best meat and vitamins, but it looks like I will never be able to run her. I tried to find the last owner again, but he seems to have disappeared from the country. I cannot afford another greyhound. It took me two years to save up for this one, so could you please help me as I am desperate.

A From your description, it appears that your bitch has not been properly looked after by the previous owner. Unfortunately, without examining the bitch it is difficult for me to diagnose any underlying cause for her problems.

Obviously, your own vet has wormed her out, and given her a course of vitamins and other tablets to pick her up. I trust that her age is correct, as being only a two-year-old, there is a very good chance that she should improve and regain her spirit. You are feeding her good quality food and adequate levels of vitamins. It is hard to say whether the last owner gave her any treatment that would have damaged her liver, or perhaps kidneys, that could slow her recovery. The loss of hair on her hindquarters suggests she has been stressed by hard racing, and with rest and care, she should improve over four to six months.

However, I would suggest two steps that may be of help. Unfortunately, many greyhounds that have been badly treated will become subdued and lack enthusiasm. This can be regained by exercising her with a younger greyhound, as it may help to rejuvenate her interest in life. In some cases, where a single greyhound is walked and exercised without contact with other dogs, they become withdrawn. Therefore, I would suggest that you try and walk and exercise your bitch with a friend who has a more energetic greyhound.

Secondly, a course of a supplement containing caffeine, such as Fortex or other brand, may be useful to stimulate her nervous system and general awareness. I would suggest that you give the equivalent of about 100mg of caffeine a day with her food, for the first 4-5 days, reducing this by 20mg a day over the next week or two. This will help to stimulate her metabolism, nervous reactions, and this, combined with the example set by a younger more energetic greyhound, may help to overcome her subdued behaviour. Also, giving her a chance to course or chase in a pack of other greyhounds may also make her more keen and lively. However, a tonic such as Fortex must be withdrawn about ten days before racing to avoid a positive swab.

With time, providing there is no internal damage, or she is much older than you have been led to believe, I feel sure she will regain her spirit, and with your own tender loving care and understanding, she should improve.

POOR CHASERS

Q **I have a litter of seven pups which are now 12 months of age. I recently started taking** **141.** **them to the schooling track to introduce them to the racing environment. However, they seem to withdraw into themselves when at the track, and they show little interest in the mechanical hare. Despite repeated visits to the track, they still seem intimidated by the track environment. I have tried hand slipping the pups without success.**

At home, the pups are, and always have been, alert and lively animals who show plenty of interest in anything which moves, and gallop freely, chasing rabbits, hares, etc. It is only at the track that the pups lose the 'fire in their bellies'. I have had this problem with the occasional pup in the past, but never the entire litter. I am now desperate. Are there are medications on the market which might give the pups the courage to overcome their problems and hopefully enjoy life at the racetrack!

A The problems your pups are experiencing are not uncommon. Some bloodlines of greyhounds, whilst being top class gallopers, are poor chasers on the race track. Often pups will chase wild game at home, but show little interest in the mechanical lure.

Studies suggest that greyhounds hunt and chase not only by sight. They use their natural five senses which all animals have to varying degrees: sight, sound, smell, touch and taste. On the track greyhounds are exposed only to the sight of an often unconvincing 'hare', which is moving at speed. Racetrack conditions are accompanied by unnatural and intimidating noise of the traps and lure mechanism. If the pups can be made to take interest in the lure by adding sound and smell, usually they are keener to chase.

Recently trainers in Australia and the USA started using an electronic device called a 'Bugs Teaser'. This teaser can be impregnated with natural 'gamey' smells and emits the sound of the hare or rabbit. Initially, pups are teased with this lure regularly from the age of three to four months onwards. Later the device is used on a drag lure at the schooling track and used to excite the pups at the traps. The teaser is then given to the pups at the catching pen or pick-up, as a reward. This method of schooling has been very successful in the USA and Australia where many tracks also have a lure which emits the noise of the natural prey of the greyhound.

Your 12-month-old pups might well benefit from the use of a 'Bugs Teaser', even at this late stage (if they are available on the British market). The pups could also benefit from a course of a caffeine based tonic, such as 6ml Fortex daily, for the duration of their schooling period, to increase their alertness and well being.